SCHOLASTIC

READ180®

NEXT*GENERATION*

D1088289

rBook®

Stage A

Table of Contents

WORKSHOPS

1 SCIENCE
Informational Text

2 SOCIAL STUDIES
Informational Text

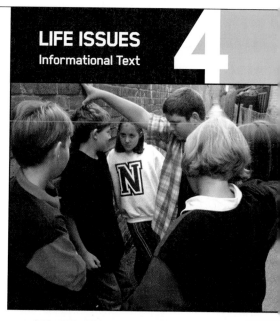

LITERATURE
Literary Text

3

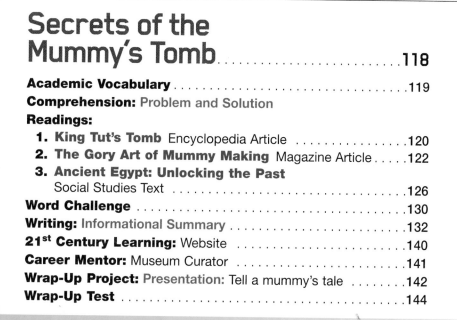

LIFE ISSUES
Informational Text

4

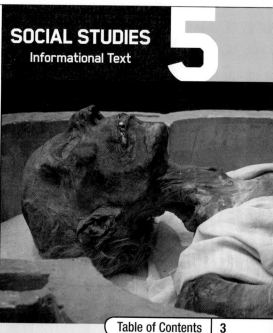

SOCIAL STUDIES
Informational Text

5

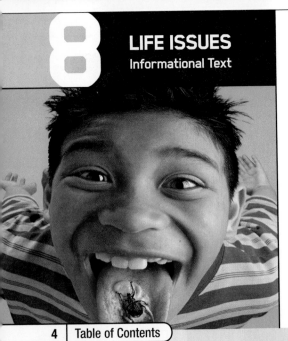

Informational Text
Literary Text
9

Your Resources

Content Area Icon Key

Ancient Civilizations   Earth Science   U.S. History   Literature   Health/Life Issues

Life Science   Science & Technology   The Arts   U.S. History   World Geography

Welcome to the *rBook*

Get ready for the *rBook* by taking this quiz. After you finish each Workshop, check back to see if your ideas or opinions have changed.

START

1 Fires Out of Control

A huge fire is headed toward your neighborhood. Read the following statements. Check the one you think is best.

❑ You should stay at home and protect your house from the fire.

❑ You should leave your house and go with your family to a shelter.

2 Coming to America

Why do you think people move to the United States from other countries? Order the reasons below.

1 = most common reason
4 = least common reason

____ People want to go to U.S. schools.

____ People like American food.

____ People have to leave their homes because of violence and war.

____ People want to start a new life in a country with a lot of freedom.

3 Bud, Not Buddy

"Bud's Breakfast," from *Bud Not Buddy*, is a story about a boy who has to take care of himself. Bud learns a lot by being on his own. Read the statements below. Check the ones you think will be true for Bud.

❑ Everyone tries to help a poor kid.

❑ People like to share what they have.

❑ It's easy for a kid to get by on his own.

4 Bullies Beware

At lunch, a classmate at your table is bullying another student. What do you do? Circle your answer.

1. Tell an adult.

2. Tell the bully to leave the student alone.

3. Keep quiet so that the bully won't say anything to me.

5 Secrets of the Mummy's Tomb

Think about the Workshop title, "Secrets of the Mummy's Tomb." Look at the photo below. What do you predict this Workshop will be about? Explain your answer.

_____

_____

_____

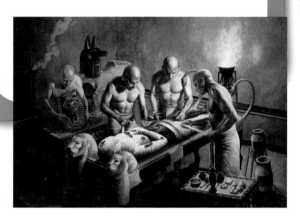

6 Good Sports

Read the statements about sports below. Write **A** if you agree. Write **D** if you disagree.

_____ Everyone has at least one sport or activity they are good at.

_____ Playing games like marbles is not very competitive.

_____ If you are not naturally talented at sports, practicing will not help you.

7 Taming Wild Beasts

Which of these animals would make a good pet? Check them.

- ☐ tiger cub
- ☐ bear cub
- ☐ dog
- ☐ cat
- ☐ bird
- ☐ elephant
- ☐ alligator
- ☐ gorilla

Circle the pet you would most like to have.

8 Food: The Good, the Bad, and the Gross

What do you think you will read about in this Workshop? Write one food in each row.

Good Food	
Bad Food	
Gross Food	

What is your favorite food?

_____

_____

9 No Small Hero

Who is someone you think is a hero?

_____

What could a kid do to become a hero?

_____

_____

_____

_____

FINISH

WORKSHOP 1

INFORMATIONAL TEXT

COMPREHENSION FOCUS
Main Idea and Details

CRITICAL READING FOCUS
Analyze

Reading 1 | Survived the Yellowstone Fire | **Personal Narrative**

Reading 2 Smoke Jumpers | **Magazine Article**

Reading 3 Up in Flames | **Science Text**

FIRES
Out of Control

Every year, wildfires burn through America's forests. Red-hot flames turn trees into blackened poles. Hot, dry winds blow sparks across thousands or even millions of acres. And when wildfires reach towns, people run for their lives.

In this Workshop, you'll find out what it's like to survive a wildfire. You'll meet firefighting heroes. You'll also discover the explosive science behind fire.

Turn the page and get ready—the heat is on!

Academic Vocabulary

Target Word	Meaning	Example
▶ Read the Target Words. Rate each one using the scale below.*	▶ Read the Target Word meanings. Write in the missing words.	▶ Finish the Target Word examples below.
rapidly (p. 13) rap•id•ly (adverb) ① ② ③ ④	moving very fast or _____	• The runner could hear _____ _____ **rapidly**. • To get to school **rapidly**, we could take _____ _____
fuel (p. 14) fu•el (noun) ① ② ③ ④	something that can be burned to produce heat or energy	• The car _____ _____ because it needed **fuel**. • _____ is a type of **fuel**.
region (p. 14) re•gion (noun) ① ② ③ ④	a _____ or _____ or country	• A warm-weather **region** in the U.S. is _____ _____ • I would like to live in a **region** of my state that _____ _____
survive (p. 17) sur•vive (verb) ① ② ③ ④	to stay alive during a dangerous event	• To **survive** a _____, I would _____ • Some people did not **survive** _____
degree (p. 18) de•gree (noun) ① ② ③ ④	a unit for measuring _____	Firefighters wear jackets that resist heat up to 700 **degrees**.

*Rating Scale
① = I don't know the word.   ③ = I think I know the word.
② = I've seen it or heard it.   ④ = I know it and use it.

The Key Idea

▶ **WRITE** What is this personal narrative mostly about?

_____

_____

Target Word

approach

ap•proach (verb)

Rate It: ① ② ③ ④

Meaning

to move _____

Example

It would be _____

to **approach** _____

_____

_____

React and Write

▶ **WRITE** What might be scary about seeing a wildfire up close? What might be interesting?

Summarize

In one or two sentences, summarize what happened to the family in the park. Include the topic and important details.

I Survived the Yellowstone Fire

by Zoë Kashner

Deer flee the Yellowstone fire.

In 1988, when I was 13, my family went to Yellowstone National Park. We didn't go to camp. We went to see the biggest fire in the history of the park.

We heard about the fire on the way back from a camping trip. My dad was a science teacher. He thought we should see this once-in-a-lifetime fire. We took a vote. Dad won. So, we drove to Montana.

We were allowed to enter the park. It was amazing. Driving in, we saw bears fleeing the flames. Smoke filled the air. We made it to the center of the park.

Everything seemed under control. Then we heard bad news. Park rangers told us that taking the road out was too risky. We were trapped inside the park for the night! We had to share a tent with two other families. I had a hard time sleeping. Would the fire **approach** our tent? Would I ever see my home again?

In the morning, the rangers let us drive out of the park. We were safe. In fact, no one died in that fire.

When the fire finally burned out, over 1.2 million acres were burned to the ground. I'm glad I got to see the fire. I'm also glad that we made it out alive! END

Words to Know! **fleeing** running away

Comprehension Focus

Main Idea and Details

The **main idea** is the most important point about a topic. **Details** are the **facts** that support the main idea. To find the main idea and details:

- Decide what the topic is. Find the main idea about the topic.
- Look for details that support the main idea.

▶ **Complete this chart with the main idea and details of "I Survived the Yellowstone Fire."**

Detail

Zoë's dad thought the family should see the once-in-a-lifetime fire.

_____

_____

_____

Detail

_____

_____

_____

_____

Main Idea

_____

_____

_____

_____

_____

Detail

_____

_____

_____

_____

_____

Detail

_____

_____

_____

_____

_____

💡 The Key Idea

▶ **WRITE** What is this magazine article mostly about?

_____

_____

◎ VOCABULARY
Target Word

condition

con•di•tion (noun)

Rate It: ① ② ③ ④

Meaning

the general state of a _____

place, _____, or thing

Example

One **condition** smoke jumpers

face is _____

_____

❗ React and Write

▶ **WRITE** Would you be afraid to jump out of a plane with a parachute? Why or why not?

SMOKE

Smoke jumpers prepare to stop a fire.

JUMPERS

Most people run from fires.
These heroes jump into the flames.

Who do people call when forest fires start in the wilderness? Smoke jumpers. They are special firefighters. Their job is hot and tough. But it's very important.

Tough Work

Smoke jumping is a challenging job. Not just anyone can do it. Smoke jumpers have to be smart and physically fit. They must brave dangerous **conditions** when they work.

Smoke jumpers go where other firefighters can't. Many fires start deep in the woods. Without roads, trucks can't help. Instead, jumpers are dropped from planes. All their assistance must come from the air.

Safety First

Staying safe is important for smoke jumpers. Safety starts in the air. When they drop out of the planes, smoke jumpers steer their parachutes. They have to land away from the flames.

On the ground, the danger heats up rapidly. Smoke jumpers can get trapped. So, they wear clothes that won't burn. They also carry tents that won't catch on fire. That way, they can hide inside the tents. They can sweat it out until the fire passes. ➤

Words to Know!	**assistance**	help

Main Idea and Details

1. ▶ **WRITE** What is the main idea in "Tough Work"?

_____

_____

2. UNDERLINE What are two important details that support the main idea in "Tough Work"?

3. ▶ **WRITE** What is the main idea in "Safety First"?

_____

_____

4. UNDERLINE Identify two important details that support the main idea in "Safety First."

CRITICAL READING
Analyze

1. ✔ **CHECK** Mark two conditions that make a smoke jumper's job especially dangerous.

2. ▶ **WRITE** For one of the conditions that you marked, explain what makes it so dangerous.

_____

_____

_____

Active Reading

<u>UNDERLINE</u> What do smoke jumpers do if everything else fails?

VOCABULARY
Target Word

locate

lo•cate (verb)

Rate It: ① ② ③ ④

Meaning

to _____ something

Example

People can **locate** a fire by

_____

_____

React and Write

 WRITE What would be cool about being a smoke jumper? What might not be so cool?

Summarize

In one or two sentences, summarize the topic and important details in "Getting the Job Done."

A smoke jumper prepares to parachute into a burning forest.

Getting the Job Done

How do smoke jumpers do their job? They don't have big hoses. They don't have huge trucks. But they know other ways to fight fire.

Sometimes, smoke jumpers fight fire with fire. How? They start a "back burn." This method burns the trees in the fire's path. Then the fire has no fuel to burn. The fire can't spread.

Some jumpers dig a ditch to stop a fire. The ditch is called a "fire line." To make the fire line, jumpers cut down trees. They also dig up bushes. Finally, a big dirt ditch divides the region on fire from the rest of the forest. When the fire reaches the ditch, there's nothing to burn. So it stops spreading.

Smoke jumpers also get help from above. How? Planes scoop up water from a lake or another nearby source. Then, they fly over the fire. When the pilot **locates** the fire, they dump the water to keep the fire from spreading.

If nothing else works, jumpers have to wait for rain. Rain can put a fire out for good.

Smoke jumping is very exciting. But this career is far from easy. The next time you hear about a forest fire, you'll know the heroes who are coming to the rescue—the smoke jumpers. ⟨END⟩

| Words to Know! | **method** way of doing something |

Earth Science

Comprehension Focus
Main Idea and Details

▶ Complete this chart with the main idea and details in "Getting the Job Done."

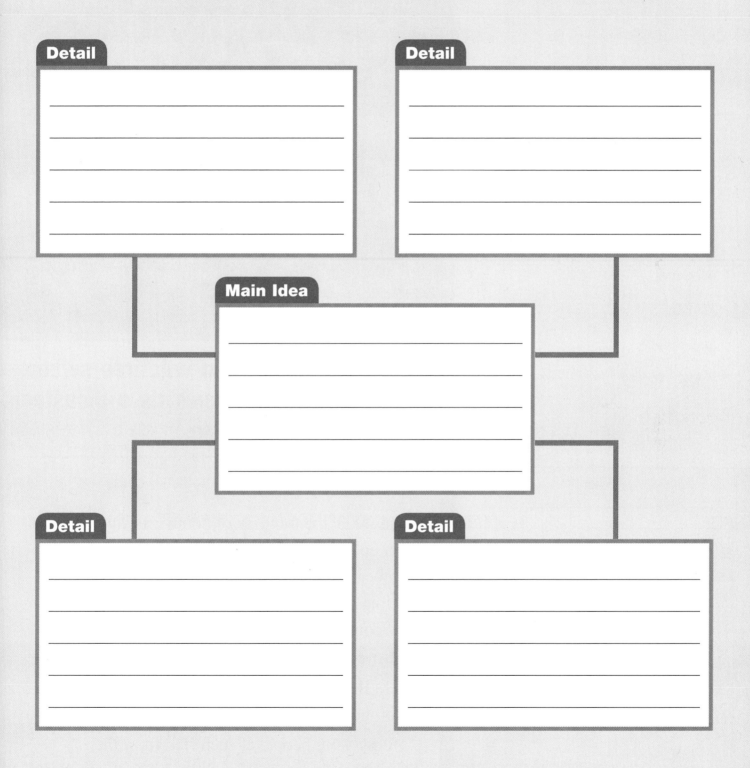

Detail

Detail

Main Idea

Detail

Detail

💡 The Key Idea

▶ **WRITE** What is this science text mostly about?

_____

_____

_____

◎ VOCABULARY Target Word

rebuild

re•build (verb)

Rate It: ① ② ③ ④

Meaning

to build _____

Example

After a fire, people need to

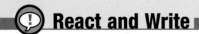 rebuild their _____

_____

_____

❗ React and Write

▶ **WRITE** What things would you want to take with you if your house were on fire?

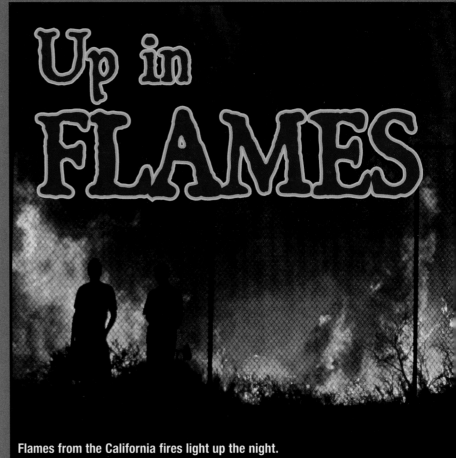

Up in FLAMES

Flames from the California fires light up the night.

What happens when wildfires sweep across 750,000 acres? It's a disaster that's too hot to handle.

A State on Fire

In 2003, the foothills of Southern California went up in flames. The first fires began in late October. Within days, 14,000 firefighters were battling a dozen blazes! Sometimes, there was little they could do. They could only watch as flames destroyed homes and jumped over freeways.

In the end, more than 20 people died. Almost 3,000 houses burned down.

Why were people at such risk from the fires? It's because many homes are in the foothills.

They are surrounded by trees. There are only a few windy roads to get out.

Fire Survivors

In many places, people escaped early. Firefighters went door-to-door. They told people to leave their homes for safety.

People went to friends' homes or hotels. Shelters were set up away from the fire. In San Bernardino, almost 2,000 people fled to a huge building that used to house airplanes.

Others had to rapidly race away from their burning homes. Many drove down roads with flames high on both sides.

But not everyone left home in time. One family found itself trapped. They survived the fire by diving into their swimming pool. The windows of their house exploded in front of them.

The 2003 fires blazed for nearly a month. Then, in November, the rain came. The fires finally fizzled out. But the damage was done. California had to spend more than $250 million fighting the fires. It would take billions more to **rebuild** lost property. And the 22 lives lost could never be replaced. ➤

Words to Know! **foothills** low hills at the base of mountains

📖 Main Idea and Details

1. ▣▷ **WRITE** Find the main idea in "A State on Fire."

_____

_____

2. **UNDERLINE** Mark two important details in "A State on Fire."

3. ▣▷ **WRITE** Identify the main idea in "Fire Survivors."

_____

_____

4. **UNDERLINE** Find two important details in "Fire Survivors."

CRITICAL READING
🧠 Analyze

1. ✔ **CHECK** Find three actions people took to escape the fire.

2. ▣▷ **WRITE** How could an escape plan have helped the trapped family?

_____

_____

_____

_____

REVIEW
📖 Read for Detail

⬭CIRCLE⬭ Mark a detail that tells when the fire finally ended.

Active Reading

★**STAR** How hot can it get during California summers?

VOCABULARY
Target Word

challenge

chal•lenge (noun)

Rate It: ① ② ③ ④

Meaning

something that is _____ to do

Example

One **challenge** I face each day

is _____

_____.

React and Write

▶ **WRITE** Think about your home. How safe is it from fire?

Summarize

▶ **WRITE** Summarize the topic and important details in the science text "Up in Flames."

How Fires Start

The wildfires of 2003 could happen again. California has all the necessary conditions for fires to go out of control. It has fuel, oxygen, and heat.

Fuel is anything that can burn easily. Dry trees, leaves, logs, or twigs are fuel. A common fuel in California is thick brush called chaparral. Chaparral burns quickly at high-degree temperatures. It grows over most of the California foothills.

Fires also need oxygen. Oxygen is part of the air. Wind feeds a fire extra oxygen. This makes the fire burn hotter. Wind can also help a fire spread. Places that are windy often suffer more fire damage. California is very windy. The Santa Ana winds, which come every fall, are very strong.

A fire also needs heat. California is famous for its sunshine. In the summer, temperatures often hit 100 degrees. Dry brush burns easily in hot weather. A lightning strike can also start a wildfire.

 TEXT FEATURE Reading a Diagram

The Fire Triangle

OXYGEN

FUEL

HEAT

Fires vs. Firefighters

Saving homes from wildfires is a **challenge**. Firefighters have little warning when fires are coming. They must work fast to save what they can.

First, firefighters mark houses "winners" and "losers." A log cabin with shrubs around it is a loser. It is made of fuel for the fire, and probably can't be saved. A stone home with few plants around it would probably be a winner, much easier to save.

To save houses, firefighters create "defensible space." They clear away plants and other fuel. They also bulldoze yards to create gaps that fire can't jump.

Then the fire hits. Some houses will burn to the ground. Others will remain untouched. Why? Often, the wind or weather changes directions. In addition, some houses are made out of nonflammable materials. Others are highly flammable.

Once the fire is out, people can begin to rebuild. But the fear of next year's fires still remains. END

Words to Know! **defensible** able to be defended

A diagram is a drawing or plan that explains something.

❶ According to this diagram, what do fires need to burn?

Ⓐ fuel   Ⓒ fuel, oxygen, and heat

Ⓑ fuel and oxygen   Ⓓ oxygen and heat

❷ What happens if you remove oxygen from a fire?

Ⓐ It burns brighter.   Ⓒ It turns into gold.

Ⓑ It goes out.   Ⓓ It burns hotter.

❸ **Analyze:** Why is this diagram called "The Fire Triangle"?

_____

_____

Main Idea and Details

1. ▶ **WRITE** What is the main idea in "How Fires Start"?

_____

_____

2. **UNDERLINE** Identify two important details in that section.

CRITICAL READING
Analyze

▶ **WRITE** When fire hits, some houses burn and others remain untouched. Why?

_____

_____

_____

_____

_____

_____

Skills Check

1. ▶ **WRITE** What is the main idea in "Fires vs. Firefighters"?

_____

_____

2. **UNDERLINE** Mark two important details in that section.

Word Challenge

Start

1 Number them.

How **rapidly** would each food disappear from your fridge?

1 = most **rapidly**
4 = least **rapidly**

____ leftover pizza

____ leftover mac 'n' cheese

____ leftover birthday cake

____ cat food

2 Prefixes

A **prefix** is a letter or a group of letters added to the beginning of a word. A prefix changes the meaning of a word. The prefix *re-* means "again." So *redo* means "to do again." The prefix *un-* can mean *not*. *Unbroken* means "not broken."

Define. Each of these words has the prefix *re-* or *un-*. Write what each word means, based on the meaning of its prefix. Then use a dictionary to check your work.

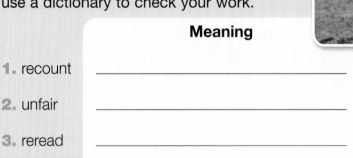

One more hit, and our rivals will **regain** their lead!

Meaning

1. recount _____

2. unfair _____

3. reread _____

4. unable _____

3 Identify them.

Circle three places that are **regions** (instead of cities or states).

Texas

Chicago, Illinois

The Great Plains

The Northwest

California

The East Coast

Miami, Florida

4 Analyze.

What would you wear outside when the temperature is 10 **degrees** below zero F? Check one or more.

☐ scarf   ☐ T-shirt

☐ mittens   ☐ sandals

What would you wear outside when the temperature is 99 **degrees** F? Check one or more.

☐ ski cap   ☐ flip-flops

☐ shorts   ☐ sweater

5 **Rank them.** Which would use the most **fuel**?

1 = the least **fuel**

3 = the most **fuel**

____ flying a plane across the country

____ heating a can of soup

____ using a boat to pull two water skiers across a lake

6 **Check them.** Which of these events might cause someone to **rebuild** a house?

☐ a busy yard sale

☐ a huge tornado

☐ a light rain

☐ a major flood

7 **Describe.** What is a good way to **approach** a new student at your school?

_____

_____

What is a terrible way to **approach** a new student at your school?

_____

_____

8 **Suffixes**

A **suffix** is a letter or a group of letters added to the end of a word. A suffix changes the meaning or part of speech of a word. The suffixes -er and -or mean "a person or thing connected with." These suffixes turn verbs into nouns. *Drive* is a verb. *Driver* is a noun.

Add the suffix -er to turn these verbs into nouns.

read: _____

bank: _____

work: _____

Add the suffix -or to turn these verbs into nouns.

sail: _____

survive: _____

investigate: _____

This **reader** reads books using a special alphabet for the blind called Braille.

9 **Analyze.** What are the best weather **conditions** for each of these outdoor activities?

swimming in a lake: _____

building a snowman: _____

riding a bike: _____

10 **Tell about it.** Complete the sentences using **locate**, **survive**, and **challenge**.

I wasn't sure I would _____ my first day at a

new school. First, it was a real _____

to open my locker. Then I couldn't _____

the lunchroom. When I did, the lunch was gross!

Writing Text Type

Explanatory Paragraph

An **explanatory paragraph** provides information and explains it.

▶ **Read Julia's explanatory paragraph about the job of a forest ranger.**

Student Model

Topic Sentence

The **topic sentence** states the main topic of the paragraph.

1. UNDERLINE the **topic sentence**.

A strong topic sentence includes a **controlling idea** that makes the writer's point about the topic.

2. BOX the **controlling idea**.

Detail Sentences

Factual details in the paragraph support the topic sentence with **facts and examples**.

3. ✔ CHECK three **facts or examples**.

Language Use

Linking words and phrases introduce and connect ideas.

4. CIRCLE four **linking words or phrases** that introduce or connect ideas.

Concluding Sentence

The **concluding sentence** sums up the topic.

5. ★ STAR the concluding sentence.

Keeping Forests Safe
by Julia Rodriguez

Being a forest ranger is a challenging job. To start with, forest rangers must be physically fit. They have to walk many miles in parks every day. They often have to rebuild trails and campsites. In addition, a forest ranger has to know a lot about the region where he or she works. Most rangers can identify all the plants and animals in their forests. Some forest rangers run workshops to tell visitors about their park. Most importantly, rangers must keep campers safe. They protect campers if a fire or storm approaches. In conclusion, being a forest ranger is a tough job with many responsibilities.

B *I* U

P 1

Brainstorm

▶ Read the writing prompt. Then use the boxes to help you brainstorm ideas.

What Firefighters Do

What Firefighters Know

Writing Prompt:
Explain why firefighting is a challenging job.

Dangers Firefighters Face

Equipment Firefighters Use

Choose Your Topic

▶ Select one of your ideas from the idea web. Complete the sentence below.

I plan to write about _____ because it explains

_____

Organize Ideas for Writing

▶ **Complete this outline with notes for your explanatory paragraph.**

I. Topic Sentence. State your main topic.

Topic: _____

Controlling Idea: _____

II. Detail Sentences. List two factual details that support the topic sentence.

Detail 1: _____

Detail 2: _____

III. Concluding Sentence. Sum up the topic in a concluding sentence.

_____

_____

Write Your Draft

▶ **Write a draft of your explanatory paragraph.**

Writing Prompt:
Explain why firefighting is a challenging job.

WORD CHOICES	
Everyday	**Precise**
find	locate, identify
help	assist, aid
check	inspect, examine

_____
(title)

▶ **Write your topic sentence.**

Topic Sentence

Firefighting is _____
(topic)

because _____
(controlling idea)

▶ **Type your topic sentence on the computer or write it on paper. Then use these linking words and phrases to complete a draft of your paragraph.**

Detail Sentences

To start with, . . .	*For example, . . .*
Another . . .	*Also, . . .*

Concluding Sentence

In conclusion, . . .	*To sum up, . . .*

Revise Your Paragraph

▶ **Evaluate: Rate your paragraph. Then have a writing partner rate it.**

Scoring Guide			
needs improvement	average	good	excellent
1	2	3	4

1. **UNDERLINE** the topic sentence. Does it state the main topic of the paragraph?

   Self   1   2   3   4

   Partner 1   2   3   4

2. **BOX** the controlling idea. Does it make a point about the topic?

   Self   1   2   3   4

   Partner 1   2   3   4

3. ✔**CHECK** details. Do factual details support the topic sentence with facts and examples?

   Self   1   2   3   4

   Partner 1   2   3   4

4. **CIRCLE** linking words and phrases. Do they introduce or connect ideas?

   Self   1   2   3   4

   Partner 1   2   3   4

5. ★**STAR** the concluding sentence. Does it sum up the topic?

   Self   1   2   3   4

   Partner 1   2   3   4

▶ **Discuss: Give feedback on your partner's explanatory paragraph.**

1. Start with a positive comment about your partner's explanatory paragraph.

   You clearly explain _____

   _____

   The way you _____

   _____ is interesting.

2. Give your partner suggestions for revision.

   You should include details that _____

   _____

   Your paragraph would be stronger if

   you _____

   _____

3. Answer any questions your partner has about your suggestions.

4. Ask your partner for feedback. Use the frames below to summarize your partner's feedback.

   I clearly explained . . .
   You found the way I . . . interesting.
   I should include details that . . .
   My paragraph would be stronger if . . .

▶ **Revise: Now, revise your explanatory paragraph.**

Grammar IDENTIFYING SENTENCES AND FRAGMENTS

A **sentence** tells a complete idea. Every sentence has two parts.

- The **subject** tells who or what the sentence is about.
- The predicate tells what someone or something does.

Examples

Subject	Predicate
The bears	escaped the fire.
The raging fires	burned everything around them.

▶ **Identify the underlined part of each sentence below. Write *subject* or *predicate* on the line beside it.**

1. Smoke jumpers <u>have very dangerous jobs</u>.   *predicate*

2. An airplane <u>carries them to forest fires</u>.

3. Then <u>these firefighters</u> leap from airplanes.

4. They <u>steer their parachutes away from the flames</u>.

5. <u>The heat and smoke</u> make working difficult.

A **sentence fragment** is an incomplete sentence that cannot stand by itself. Often, a fragment is missing a subject or a predicate.

Examples

Fragment	Complete Sentence
wear brightly colored clothes **[missing a subject]**	Smoke jumpers wear brightly colored clothes.
In order to burn, fires **[missing a predicate]**	In order to burn, fires need heat, oxygen, and fuel.

▶ **Rewrite the sentence fragments below as complete sentences.**

6. put out many forest fires last year

_____

7. the brave smoke jumpers

_____

8. lots of heavy equipment

_____

▶ **Edit Your Draft.** Take a close look at each of the sentences in your draft. **Do they all explain a complete idea?** Fix any that do not.

Mechanics USING END PUNCTUATION

Different kinds of sentences use different end punctuation marks.

- A **statement** always ends with a period.
- A **question** always ends with a question mark.

Examples

Statement	Question
Firefighters have to be brave.	Do you know a firefighter?
A fire station is down the street.	Have you ever seen a fire?

▶ **Find and correct five errors in this paragraph.**

Student Model

Being a forest ranger is hard. Why is this job. A big challenge. First, forest rangers must know their reigons well. They must find lost campers? Also, forest rangers must warn campers about weather condishons. In addition, they have to be brave. If a bear attacks a camper, they have to handle it. In conclusion, forest rangers have tough jobs.

CHECK AND CORRECT

☐ Correct one sentence fragment.

☐ **UNDERLINE** two end punctuation errors and correct them.

☐ (CIRCLE) two spelling errors and correct them.

▶ **Edit Your Draft.** Look at the sentences in your draft. **Do they all have correct end punctuation?** Fix any that don't.

Final Draft/Present

▶ **Write a final draft of your paragraph on paper or the computer. Check it again and correct any errors before you present it.**

Focus Skill   Gather Information

Read an Evacuation Plan

If a fire broke out in your home, would you know how to get out safely? Does your family have an evacuation plan? This is one family's plan for escaping a fire.

▶ **Read the evacuation plan. Then answer the questions.**

MARK IT

- **CIRCLE** three exits.
- ★ **STAR** the three smoke alarms.
- **BOX** the Fire Department emergency number.

SMITH FAMILY EVACUATION PLAN

(5A) Smoke Alarm
EXIT Door or Exit
⎯ Window
Meeting Place

Oak Tree Next Door

Fire Department Emergency Number: ___123-555-0199 or 911___

---

① **What is this family's chosen meeting place?**

Ⓐ the main hallway in the apartment

Ⓑ the fire escape in the kitchen

Ⓒ the fire department across the street

Ⓓ a tree a safe distance from the building

② **How many fire escapes lead from the Smiths' apartment?**

Ⓐ 1   Ⓒ 3

Ⓑ 2   Ⓓ 4

③ **Many house fires start in kitchens. How would you escape a kitchen fire in the Smiths' apartment? What would determine your escape route?**

_____

_____

_____

_____

_____

Fire Marshal
Shelby Irving

Meet a fire marshal who enforces fire codes and teaches fire safety.

▶ **Read the daily work log and job information. Then answer the questions below about Shelby Irving's job.**

9 AM A call came in about a fire in progress. I don't fight fires—my job is to find out what causes them. I examined the scene and talked to firefighters and eyewitnesses. It turns out that a pan burned when it was left on the stove for too long. The entire kitchen was destroyed.

11 AM Inspected a new clothing store to make sure fire codes were being followed. The fire sprinklers worked and fire exits were clear, so the store passed the inspection.

1 PM For fire prevention week, I visited a grade school. We brought a specially designed house on a trailer. We filled the house with fake smoke so that kids could practice fire safety in a realistic setting. Taught the children fire safety rules and how to call 911 in an emergency.

5 PM I wrote up an information sheet about this morning's fire and sent it to all area newspapers. Then, I finished up paperwork before the end of the day.

❶ **How does Shelby gather information at the scene of a fire? Who does she talk to?**

_____

_____

❷ **How dangerous do you think Shelby's job is? Mark the line.**

1   2   3   4   5

Not very dangerous   Very dangerous

❸ **Shelby's job is / isn't** (circle one) **dangerous because**

_____

ON THE JOB

LOCATION

Danville, Virginia

EDUCATION

Associate's degree in Fire Engineering

RESPONSIBILITIES
- Finds the causes of fires
- Teaches fire safety
- Enforces fire codes

SKILLS
- Asking questions
- Collaborating with firefighters

SALARY

$40,000–$60,000

REWARDING PART OF THE JOB

"A student I met during Fire Safety Week saw a neighbor's house on fire. She knew exactly what to do!"

CAREER CONNECTION

Law, Public Safety, Corrections and Security
www.careerclusters.org

Related Jobs
- police detective
- security officer
- court reporter

How can you survive a wildfire?

Wildfires can be deadly. Write a FAQ about wildfires for a student website on fire safety.

❶ Brainstorm. What questions might students have about wildfires? Brainstorm questions that start with *who*, *what*, *when*, *where*, *why*, and *how*.

A. How does a wildfire start? _____

B. _____

C. _____

D. _____

E. _____

F. _____

❷ Take notes. Above, circle three questions that you can answer based on the Workshop readings. Then review the readings to find information. Take notes to help you remember important details.

Question 1: _____

_____

_____

Question 2: _____

_____

_____

Question 3: _____

_____

_____

_____

❸ **Create your FAQ page.**

AN EFFECTIVE FAQ PAGE

- ✓ includes questions readers really want answered.
- ✓ uses accurate information.
- ✓ is written in a style that is short and clear.

FAQ: How to Survive a Wildfire!

Q. How does a wildfire start?

A. ______________________________

____

____

____

____

Q. ______________________________

____

A. ______________________________

____

____

____

____

Q. ______________________________

____

A. ______________________________

____

____

____

____

This page was last updated on ________________

Comprehension

▶ **Fill in the circle next to the correct answer.**

1. The 1988 fire in Yellowstone National Park
_____.

Ⓐ killed more than 200 people

Ⓑ burned more than 1.2 million acres

Ⓒ killed a family that was trapped in the park

Ⓓ made the park close down forever

> **Here's a Tip.**
> Read all of the answer choices before answering a question.

2. One way smoke jumpers fight fires is by _____.

Ⓐ using fire trucks

Ⓑ calling 911

Ⓒ digging ditches called "fire lines"

Ⓓ reading books

3. What is the main idea of this Workshop?

Ⓐ Wildfires can't be stopped because they are out of control.

Ⓑ Firefighters are brave.

Ⓒ Every year in the U.S., firefighters must battle out-of-control wildfires.

Ⓓ Wildfires can be good for the environment.

4. Analyze: Why are many homes in California's foothills at risk?

Ⓐ The houses are made of flammable materials.

Ⓑ People start wildfires on purpose in the foothills.

Ⓒ The foothills are covered with brush that burns easily.

Ⓓ Firefighters have trouble getting water to houses there.

5. Analyze: Removing bushes from a yard is one effective way to protect a house from wildfires. Why?

Ⓐ Bushes do not burn as easily as grass does.

Ⓑ Bushes become fuel and make fires spread more rapidly.

Ⓒ Pets get injured when they hide in bushes during wildfires.

Ⓓ Fires move more quickly across empty yards.

Vocabulary

▶ **Fill in the circle next to the correct definition for each underlined word.**

1. A thermometer shows the <u>degree</u> of temperature.

   Ⓐ chill
   Ⓑ direction
   Ⓒ a unit for measuring temperature
   Ⓓ an amount of something liquid

2. The fire <u>rapidly</u> approached the house.

   Ⓐ easily
   Ⓑ slowly
   Ⓒ quickly
   Ⓓ often

3. In <u>regions</u> of California, bushes and trees become <u>fuel</u> for spreading fires.

   Ⓐ areas; something that can be burned
   Ⓑ forests; something that cannot be stopped
   Ⓒ forests; someone who breaks a law
   Ⓓ governments; wind

▶ **Fill in the correct answer to the question.**

4. What is the meaning of the prefix in the word <u>rebuild</u>?

   Ⓐ not
   Ⓑ again
   Ⓒ extra
   Ⓓ undo

▶ **Choose the best word to complete the sentence.**

5. The smoke jumper was a _____ of the wildfire.

   Ⓐ survive
   Ⓑ survival
   Ⓒ survivor
   Ⓓ surviving

Short Answer

▶ **Analyze:** Use what you've read in this Workshop to answer the question below. Check your spelling and grammar.

CRITICAL READING

What should you do if a wildfire approaches your home?

_____

_____

_____

WORKSHOP 2

INFORMATIONAL TEXT

COMPREHENSION FOCUS
Sequence of Events

CRITICAL READING FOCUS
Synthesize

Reading 1 New to the U.S. | **Profile**

Reading 2 My Journey to America |
Personal Narrative

Reading 3 A Nation of Immigrants |
Social Studies Text

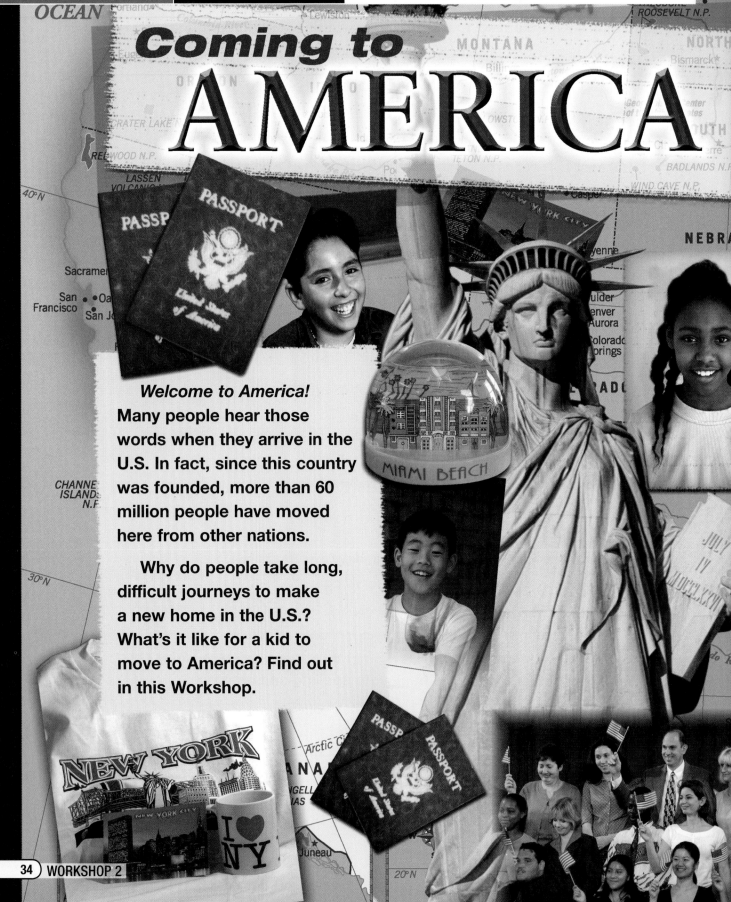

Coming to AMERICA

Welcome to America! Many people hear those words when they arrive in the U.S. In fact, since this country was founded, more than 60 million people have moved here from other nations.

Why do people take long, difficult journeys to make a new home in the U.S.? What's it like for a kid to move to America? Find out in this Workshop.

Academic Vocabulary

Target Word ▶ Read the Target Words. Rate each one using the scale below.*	Meaning ▶ Read the Target Word meanings. Write in the missing words.	Example ▶ Finish the Target Word examples below.
achieve (p. 36) a•chieve (verb) ① ② ③ ④	to _____ in doing something	• _____ is one way to **achieve** good grades. • This year, I want to **achieve** my goal of _____
journey (p. 38) jour•ney (noun) ① ② ③ ④	a long trip	• The longest **journey** that I have ever taken was to _____ _____ • _____ took a **journey** by _____
globe (p. 39) globe (noun) ① ② ③ ④	the _____	• _____ are **globe**-shaped. • I pointed out many different _____ on the **globe**.
route (p. 39) route (noun) ① ② ③ ④	a way to get from one place to another	• The **route** that I take to _____ goes past _____ • Dad takes a _____ **route** than Mom to the _____
liberty (p. 42) li•ber•ty (noun) ① ② ③ ④	a country's or a person's _____	On July 4, we celebrate our nation's **liberty** from Great Britain.

*Rating Scale
① = I don't know the word. ③ = I think I know the word.
② = I've seen it or heard it. ④ = I know it and use it.

The Key Idea

 WRITE What is this profile mostly about?

_____

_____

VOCABULARY
Target Word

translate

trans•late (verb)

Rate It: ① ② ③ ④

Meaning

to change _____ from

one _____ to another

Example

If my classmate didn't speak

English, I might **translate**

_____

_____

 React and Write

 WRITE What helps you to feel at home in a new place? Explain your response.

 Summarize

In one or two sentences, summarize what Jair did to learn to feel at home in the U.S. Include the topic and important details.

New to the U.S.

The U.S. was a whole new world for Jair. Find out how he made himself at home.

It's hard moving to a new country—especially for a kid. When Jair Saenz was in grade school, his family moved from Peru, a country in South America. They settled in Akron, Pennsylvania.

At first, Jair didn't like his new home. He couldn't understand English. He couldn't speak to his classmates. He felt all alone.

Then, Jair made friends with a student who spoke Spanish. Jair's friend **translated** sentences for him. Jair also enrolled in a special class to learn English.

Next, Jair joined the soccer team. He had loved playing soccer in Peru. Playing in the U.S. helped him learn English rapidly. Jair and his teammates shouted directions to each other as they passed the ball.

Jair plays soccer with a friend.

Soon, his new teammates were his new friends.

Now, Jair feels at home in America. He has achieved his goal of learning English. He has friends. And on the soccer field, he hears a familiar sound from home: the roar of the crowd when he scores a goal! END

Words to Know! **enrolled** signed up for

Comprehension Focus

Sequence of Events

Sequence is the order in which events happen. To find a sequence of events:

- Try to remember the order in which events take place.
- Look for times, dates, and signal words, such as *first*, *then*, *next*, *after*, and *finally*.
- When you know the order, check it again. Make sure it makes sense.

▶ **Complete this chart with the sequence of events that tell about Jair's new life in the U.S.**

At first

Jair didn't like his new home.

Then

Next

Now

The Key Idea

▶ **WRITE** What is this personal narrative mostly about?

_____

_____

_____

VOCABULARY
Target Word

voyage

voy•age (noun)

Rate It: ① ② ③ ④

Meaning

a _____ trip, especially

by _____ or spacecraft

Example

I'd like to take a **voyage** to

_____

_____

React and Write

▶ **WRITE** Virpal and her sister traveled alone for 13 hours. Would you be afraid to do that? Why or why not?

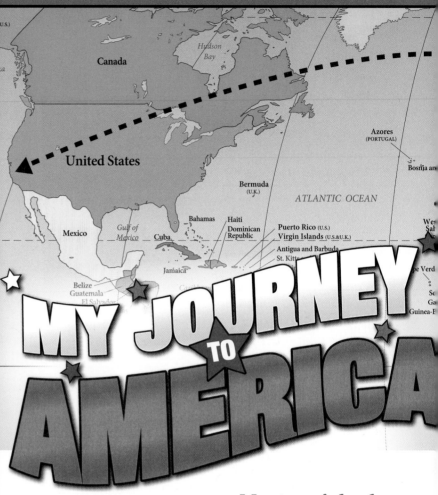

MY JOURNEY TO AMERICA

Virpal and her sister lived in Punjab, India. Their mom lived in the United States. After five years apart, the girls took a voyage to reach their mother. The journey to America wasn't easy. This is Virpal's story in her own words.

Meet a girl who traveled across the world to join her mom in America.

Left Behind

My name is Virpal. I am 13 years old. I come from Punjab, India. Five years ago, my mom was granted a visa to move to America. My sister and I stayed behind in India. We lived with other family members. Not a day went by that I didn't dream about being back together with my mother. After five years, the United States granted my sister and me permission to come live with our mother again.

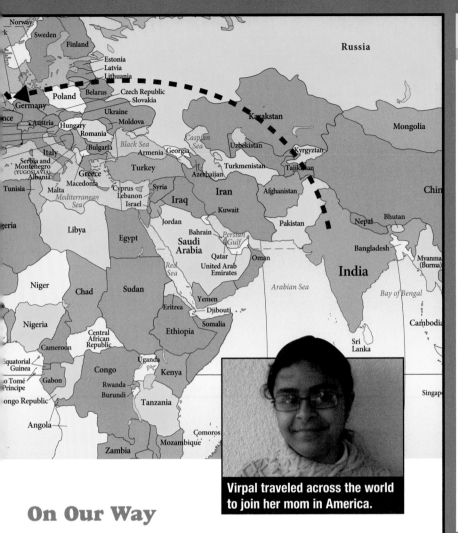

Virpal traveled across the world to join her mom in America.

On Our Way

Our **voyage** across the globe started in Delhi, India. We made several stops along the route. First, we flew on a plane to Holland. There, we had to board another airplane. But that plane was delayed for four hours. My sister and I were hungry and thirsty. And we didn't have any money.

That wasn't our only problem. Next, an airport guard pulled me aside. He wanted to investigate a box that I was carrying. It was pretty obvious that my sister and I were from a different country. Luckily, while living in India, I took English classes. The airport worker understood some English, too. So, I was able to speak with him. I told him that the box was filled with sweets for my mother. ➤

Words to Know!	**delayed** made late

Sequence of Events

1. ▶ **WRITE** Finish the sentences to tell about two events from "Left Behind."

• Five years ago, Virpal's mother

_____

_____

_____

• After five years, _____

_____

_____

_____

2. <u>UNDERLINE</u> What did Virpal do when she was stopped by an airport worker?

CRITICAL READING
Synthesize

▶ **WRITE** How does the map help you to understand the girls' journey?

_____

_____

_____

_____

Active Reading

UNDERLINE Who helped Virpal to find her mother?

VOCABULARY
Target Word

familiar

fa•mil•iar *(adjective)*

Rate It: ① ② ③ ④

Meaning

_____

_____

Example

Two places that are **familiar** to me are _____

_____

_____

React and Write

▶ **WRITE** Do you think Virpal will continue to be happy in America, or will she wish she could go back to India? Use evidence from the reading in your response.

Summarize

In one or two sentences, summarize the topic and important details in "Almost There."

Virpal's family settled in Fresno, California.

Almost There

Four hours later, my sister and I boarded the plane for America. By this time, we were so tired and hungry that we were crying on the plane.

When we landed at the Los Angeles airport, I was so happy! But as soon as we got off the airplane, we were told to get in a long line. It felt like the longest wait ever. My sister and I began to worry. We were afraid our mother might think we didn't make it. We thought she might leave the airport before our reunion. Finally, an officer from the airport helped us find her. At last, our voyage was over.

Together at Last

That day was the happiest day of my life. Finally, I saw my mother again! It was great to see her **familiar** face. Today, I am a 7th-grade student in Fresno, California. I am in Mrs. Tracy's class, and I'm achieving my goal of reading and writing in English. I am also learning to love my new country. I didn't know America would be so beautiful! END

Words to Know!	**reunion** a gathering of people who know each other

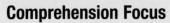

Comprehension Focus

Sequence of Events

▶ Complete the chart with four important events from Virpal's journey to America. You'll find them in the sections "On Our Way" and "Almost There."

First

Next

Four hours later

Finally

💡 The Key Idea

▶ **WRITE** What is this social studies text mostly about?

_____

_____

🎯 VOCABULARY
Target Word

seek

seek (verb)

Rate It: ① ② ③ ④

Meaning

to _____ for

Example

I like to **seek** advice from

_____

_____

_____

❗ React and Write

▶ **WRITE** Are there new immigrants in your community? Where are they from?

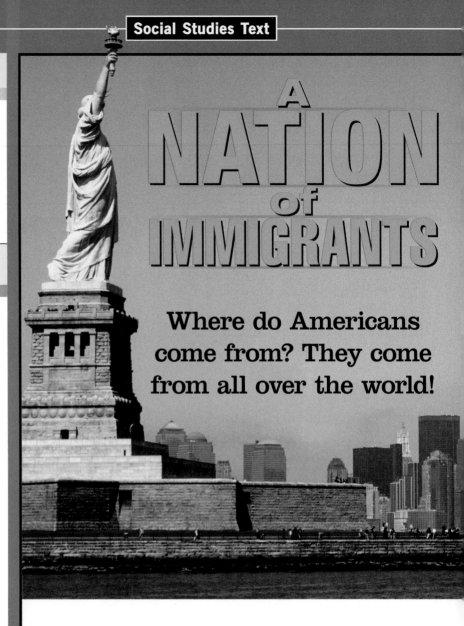

A NATION of IMMIGRANTS

Where do Americans come from? They come from all over the world!

The First Americans

An immigrant is someone who moves from one country to another. The United States is a nation of immigrants! Throughout history, more than 60 million people have made the journey to America. And new immigrants are still coming today. They want good jobs. They want a better education. They are also **seeking** liberty.

The first people to live in America were Native Americans. They lived here for thousands of years. Then, in the 1500s and 1600s, European explorers came. They were English, French, Spanish, and Dutch. They built cities like New York and Boston.

The world-famous Statue of Liberty stands in New York Harbor to welcome travelers.

During this time, millions of Africans also came to America. They were brought to the United States against their will—as slaves.

New Arrivals

The first major wave of immigration happened from 1845 to 1855. Millions of immigrants moved to America. Nearly two million came from Ireland alone. That country was suffering from a famine. More than one million others came from Germany.

The next great wave of immigration lasted from 1891 to 1901. Millions of Asians, Italians, Greeks, Jews, and Slavs moved to the U.S.

Today, there are 38 million immigrants living in the U.S. From 1981 to 1990 more than eight million immigrants arrived! Over half were from Central and South America and Mexico. But they were not the first Spanish-speaking people to come here. ➤

This immigrant family arrived in the United States in the 1890s.

Words to Know! **famine** ongoing and widespread hunger

Sequence of Events

1. **CIRCLE** What happened between 1845 and 1855?

2. ▶ **WRITE** What groups came to the U.S. between 1891 and 1901?

_____

_____

_____

REVIEW
Main Idea and Details

1. **CIRCLE** Find the main idea in "The First Americans."

2. **UNDERLINE** Mark a detail that supports this main idea.

CRITICAL READING
Synthesize

▶ **WRITE** People from many countries move to the United States. What reasons do many immigrants have in common?

_____

_____

_____

Active Reading

<u>UNDERLINE</u> Which states did many Mexicans move to in the 1700s and 1800s?

VOCABULARY
Target Word

culture

cul•ture (noun)

Rate It: ① ② ③ ④

Meaning

the _____ ideas,

and _____ of a

group of people

Example

One food that is popular in

American **culture** is _____

_____.

React and Write

▶ **WRITE** Imagine moving to another country. What would you miss most about America?

Summarize

▶ **WRITE** Summarize the topic and important details in the social studies text "A Nation of Immigrants."

History of Hispanic Immigration

Spanish settlers first came to Florida almost 450 years ago. In 1565, Pedro Menéndez de Avilés, a Spanish explorer, founded the city of St. Augustine in Florida. It is the oldest city in the United States. In 1598, Spanish settlers arrived in New Mexico. There, they established the capital city of Santa Fe.

During the 1700s and 1800s, Hispanic immigration continued. Mexicans moved to Texas, Arizona, and California. By 1900, the Mexican-American population was about 400,000.

After that, the mid-1900s saw the next big group of Hispanics coming to the U.S. During this time, large numbers of Puerto Ricans moved to the U.S. mainland. In the 1960s, there was political unrest in Cuba. Cuban immigration to the U.S. rose. Today, Hispanics account for more than one-third of all U.S. immigrants.

TEXT FEATURE Reading a Circle Graph

Hispanic Immigrants to the U.S.

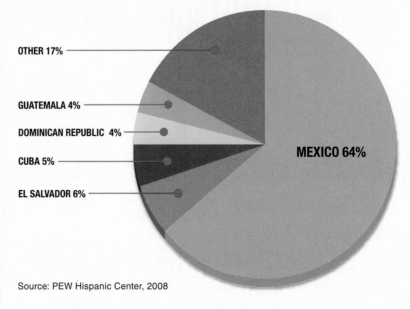

OTHER 17%

GUATEMALA 4%

DOMINICAN REPUBLIC 4%

CUBA 5%

EL SALVADOR 6%

MEXICO 64%

Source: PEW Hispanic Center, 2008

The American flag is a symbol of pride in our country.

Immigration Today

Today, Hispanic-Americans are the fastest-growing minority group in the United States. They come from many different countries and **cultures**. Immigrants from Asia are also arriving in large numbers. They come from countries such as China, Vietnam, Laos, and Thailand.

All immigrants leave something behind—family, a home, a way of life. But they also bring things with them. New foods, music, and traditions from around the world change our country every year. _END_

A circle graph shows percentages of a whole.

① Where do most Hispanic immigrants come from?

Ⓐ Mexico   Ⓒ the U.S.

Ⓑ Cuba   Ⓓ Guatemala

② What percentage of Hispanic immigrants come from El Salvador?

Ⓐ 17   Ⓑ 6   Ⓒ 5   Ⓓ 4

③ **Synthesize:** Use information from the graph to write a statement about immigration to the U.S.

_____

_____

 **Sequence of Events**

1. (CIRCLE) When did Spanish settlers first come to America?

2. ✔CHECK Mark two sentences about immigration to the U.S. today.

CRITICAL READING
Synthesize

▶WRITE Give two examples of new foods, music, and traditions that immigrants brought to the U.S.

_____

_____

_____

Skills Check

1. ▶WRITE What happened in the 1960s?

_____

2. ▶WRITE Number these events in sequence from 1 to 3.

____ The Mexican-American population was about 400,000.

____ St. Augustine was founded.

____ Cubans came to the U.S.

WORD CHALLENGE

START

1

Rate them. How **familiar** are these foods?

1 = not **familiar** at all
2 = tried it once or twice
3 = very **familiar**

____ french fries

____ pad thai

____ meat loaf

____ burrito

2 Synonyms

Synonyms are pairs of words that have similar meanings. Examples are *fast* and *quick,* or *pretty* and *beautiful*.

Draw a line from each word to its synonym.

journey	find
region	voyage
locate	area
liberty	freedom

This game is **great**!

You two say the same thing about every game.

This game is **awesome**!

3

Judge them. Rate these **journeys**.

1 = most exciting
4 = least exciting

____ taking a train cross-country

____ hiking to the top of a mountain

____ visiting another country

____ going to a local park with friends

4

Name it. Name one item you might **seek** in each of these places.

a pet store _____

a grocery store _____

a sports store _____

a clothing store _____

5 Tell about it.

Tell about it. Use these words to finish the sentences: **route**, **seek**, **globe**.

Hundreds of years ago, sailors decided to _____ a path around the world. Magellan was the first explorer to find such a _____. It took him and his crew three years to sail around the _____!

They finished their journey in 1522.

6 Choose and Explain.

Choose and Explain. If you could take a **voyage** anywhere:

Where would you go?
_____

Why?
_____

_____

Who would you bring with you?
_____

_____

7 Check them.

Check them. Which two goals would you *most* like to **achieve**?

☐ saving enough money for a new MP3 player

☐ getting good grades on your next report card

☐ raising your score on your favorite video game

☐ winning a spot on a TV game show

☐ learning to play a new musical instrument

8 Antonyms

Antonyms are pairs of words that have opposite meanings. Examples are *good* and *bad*, or *miserable* and *happy*.

Draw a line from each word to its antonym.

familiar	destroy
rebuild	strange
seek	avoid

A Chihuahua is a **tiny** dog. A Great Dane is a **huge** dog.

9 Write it.

Write it. **Translate** each term or symbol into English.

:) means: _____

🚭 means: _____

🚸 means: _____

C U L8R means: _____

10 Match them.

Match them. Match each food with the **culture** it comes from.

burrito	Japanese
egg roll	Chinese
pizza	Mexican
sushi	Italian

FINISH

Writing Text Type
Narrative Paragraph

A **narrative paragraph** tells a story about real or imagined events or experiences.

▶ **Read Eric's narrative paragraph about a trip to the Statue of Liberty.**

Introductory Statement

An **introductory statement** identifies the topic and establishes the point of view.

1. UNDERLINE the **introductory statement.**

Detail Sentences

Detail sentences describe events or experiences in **time order.**

2. NUMBER events 1–4 in time order.

Sensory details bring to life the setting, events, and people or characters.

3. ✔ CHECK five **sensory details.**

Language Use

Linking words and phrases connect ideas and details.

4. CIRCLE four **linking words or phrases.**

Vivid adjectives describe the experience in a lively way.

5. DOUBLE UNDERLINE three **vivid adjectives.**

Concluding Sentence

The **concluding sentence** completes the narrative in a satisfying way.

6. ★ STAR the **concluding sentence.**

Student Model

The Best Field Trip Ever
by Eric Washington

Last year, my class took an impressive trip to Liberty Island to see the Statue of Liberty. First, we set out on our journey in a boat. Our boat had a rumbling engine and a strong smell of fuel. Soon, the Statue of Liberty came into view. She was as tall as a skyscraper. Her face was huge! Next, we landed at Liberty Island. We went inside the base and looked up at the inside of the statue. It was exciting to see and touch such a famous symbol of freedom. Some of us enjoyed looking at an exhibit on the history of the statue. Finally, the boat went back to Manhattan. It was the most interesting field trip I've ever been on!

Brainstorm

▶ Read the writing prompt. Then use the boxes to help you brainstorm your ideas.

Class Trips

Writing Prompt:
Tell what happened on an interesting trip you have taken.

Trips With Family

Trips With Friends

Choose Your Topic

▶ Select one of your ideas from the idea web. Complete the sentence below.

I plan to write about _____

because _____

_____

Organize Ideas for Writing

▶ **Complete this outline with notes for your narrative paragraph.**

I. Introductory Statement. State your topic and point of view.

Topic: _____

Point of View: _____

II. Detail Sentences. List two details in time order that describe the event.

Detail 1: _____

Detail 2: _____

III. Concluding Sentence. Sum up the narrative in a satisfying way.

_____

_____

Write Your Draft

▶ **Write a draft of your narrative paragraph.**

Writing Prompt:
Tell what happened on an interesting trip you've taken.

WORD CHOICES	
Everyday	**Precise**
fun	entertaining, exciting
strange	unusual, odd
big	gigantic, enormous

_____
(title)

▶ **Write your introductory statement.**

Introductory Statement

I took a/an _____ trip to
(adjective)

see _____.
(place)

▶ **Type your introductory statement on the computer or write it on paper. Then use these linking words and phrases to complete a draft of your paragraph.**

Detail Sentences

First, . . .	*Next, . . .*
Soon after, . . .	*Later, . . .*

Concluding Sentence

In conclusion, . . .	*All in all, . . .*

Revise Your Paragraph

▶ **Evaluate: Rate your paragraph. Then have a writing partner rate it.**

Scoring Guide

needs improvement	average	good	excellent
1	2	3	4

1. **UNDERLINE** the introductory statement. Does it identify the topic and establish a point of view?

   Self   1   2   3   4

   Partner   1   2   3   4

2. **NUMBER** the events. Are they in time order?

   Self   1   2   3   4

   Partner   1   2   3   4

3. ✔**CHECK** sensory details. Do they help bring the story to life?

   Self   1   2   3   4

   Partner   1   2   3   4

4. **CIRCLE** linking words or phrases. Do they connect the ideas and details?

   Self   1   2   3   4

   Partner   1   2   3   4

5. **DOUBLE UNDERLINE** vivid adjectives. Are they lively?

   Self   1   2   3   4

   Partner   1   2   3   4

6. ★**STAR** the concluding sentence. Does it complete the narrative in a satisfying way?

   Self   1   2   3   4

   Partner   1   2   3   4

▶ **Discuss: Give feedback on your partner's narrative paragraph.**

1. Start with a positive comment about your partner's narrative paragraph.

   You did an effective job of _____

   _____

   I enjoyed reading _____

   _____

2. Give your partner suggestions for revision.

   I could picture the event better if you

   _____

   _____

   The time order would be clearer if you

   _____

   _____

3. Answer any questions your partner has about your suggestions.

4. Ask your partner for feedback. Use the frames below to summarize your partner's feedback.

   I did an effective job of . . .
   You enjoyed reading . . .
   You could picture the event better if I . . .
   The time order would be clearer if . . .

▶ **Revise: Now, revise your narrative paragraph.**

Grammar CORRECTING SENTENCE FRAGMENTS

A **sentence fragment** is an incomplete sentence. Often, sentence fragments are missing a subject or a verb. To fix some fragments, add a subject or verb to make a **complete sentence**.

Examples

Sentence Fragment	Complete Sentence
Settlers from Europe. [missing verb]	Settlers came from Europe.
Moved to America. [missing subject]	Settlers moved to America.

▶ **Write whether each fragment below is missing a subject or a verb.**

1. couldn't talk to other kids   _subject_

2. met a friend who spoke Spanish   _____

3. at first, life in Akron   _____

4. then, shouted instructions to his team   _____

5. Jair and his friends   _____

To correct some **sentence fragments**, you can connect the fragment to a complete sentence by adding a comma and any missing words.

Examples

Sentence and Fragment	Complete Sentence
Virpal's mom lived in the United States. Her grandma in India. [missing verb]	Virpal's mom lived in the United States, **and** her grandma **lived** in India.

▶ **Rewrite each sentence and fragment as one complete sentence.**

6. The family came together again. But not easy.

_____

7. Their plane was delayed. Waited for four hours.

_____

8. Finally, the sisters saw their mother. Hugged them both.

_____

9. Virpal thinks America is beautiful. Happy to be here.

_____

▶ **Edit Your Draft.** Take a close look at each of the sentences in your draft. **Are any of them sentence fragments?** Fix any that are.

Mechanics USING CAPITAL LETTERS

Some words begin with a **capital letter.**

- The first word in a sentence begins with a capital letter.
- Proper nouns begin with capital letters.

Examples

Correct	Incorrect
The girls were all alone.	the girls were all alone.
The guard asked Virpal to stop.	The guard asked virpal to stop.

▶ **Find and correct five errors in this paragraph.**

Student Model

Once, when I was ten, my family visited San francisco. At first, I was afraid to fly. Then, I calmed down. Had fun on the plane. Soon, we were walking around the most beautiful city! I really liked the big hills and streetcars. Next, we visited Chinatown. my mother spoke Chinese to the waiter. She tranlated the menu for us. In the end, it was a great journy for the whole family!

CHECK AND CORRECT

- ☐ **UNDERLINE** two capitalization errors and correct them.
- ☐ Correct one sentence fragment.
- ☐ CIRCLE two spelling errors and correct them.

▶ **Edit Your Draft.** Look at the sentences in your draft. **Do they all use capitals correctly?** Fix any that do not.

Final Draft/Present

▶ **Write a final draft of your paragraph on the computer or on paper. Check it again and correct any errors before you present it.**

Focus Skill   Make Decisions

Use a Population Map

This population map shows how many people in the western United States were born in other countries.

▶ **Read the map. Then answer the questions.**

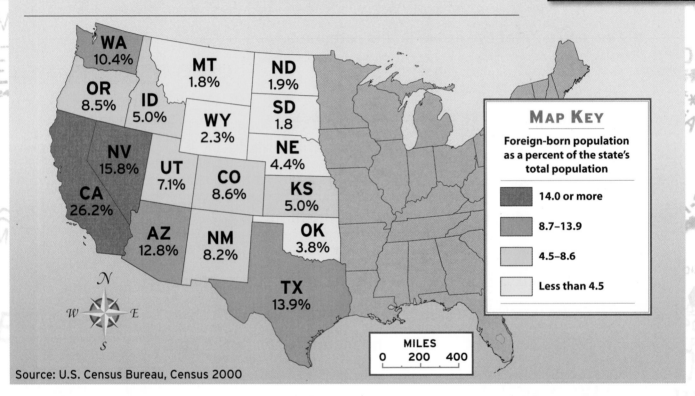

Populations of **WESTERN STATES** (Mainland)
Who Were Born in Other Nations

WA 10.4%
OR 8.5%
ID 5.0%
MT 1.8%
ND 1.9%
SD 1.8
WY 2.3%
NE 4.4%
NV 15.8%
UT 7.1%
CO 8.6%
KS 5.0%
CA 26.2%
AZ 12.8%
NM 8.2%
OK 3.8%
TX 13.9%

MAP KEY

Foreign-born population as a percent of the state's total population

	14.0 or more
	8.7–13.9
	4.5–8.6
	Less than 4.5

MILES
0   200   400

Source: U.S. Census Bureau, Census 2000

❶ **What do the numbers on the map show?**

Ⓐ the percent of people in each state who were born outside the U.S.

Ⓑ the total population of each state, in millions of people

Ⓒ the average temperature in each state

Ⓓ the size of each state in square miles

❷ **Which state has the highest percentage of people born outside the U.S.?**

Ⓐ Oklahoma   Ⓒ Nevada

Ⓑ Colorado   Ⓓ California

❸ **Use information from the map to write a sentence comparing the populations of two states.**

_____

_____

_____

_____

Community Educator
Armando Silva

Community center worker Armando Silva helps to run MECA, a community arts program for students.

▶ **Read Armando's weekly log and job information. Then answer the questions.**

Monday	Spent the morning reviewing MECA's new list of after-school classes and summer arts classes. In the afternoon, taught dance to 3rd graders. I made it fun by telling them: "Flap your arms like a bird!"
Tuesday	Met with a woman who donates money to MECA. Showed her our new schedule of classes. She likes ballet, so I told her about our exciting dance program.
Wednesday	With a designer, I created a press release to get the word out about a Latino cultural festival at MECA.
Thursday	Ran a meeting to brainstorm ideas for raising money. We always need money to start new programs and keep things running smoothly. Emailed the meeting notes to our whole staff.
Friday	Gave a tour of MECA to people who want to support us. I also invited them to the Latino cultural festival.

❶ **When Armando speaks with MECA supporters, he focuses on programs that interest them. What is an example of this?**

_____

_____

❷ **How important are listening skills in Armando's job? Mark the line.**

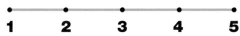

1 2 3 4 5
Not very important   **Very important**

❸ **Listening skills are/aren't** (circle one) **important because**

_____

ON THE JOB

LOCATION
Houston, Texas

EDUCATION
Bachelor's degree in Dance

RESPONSIBILITIES
• Teaches
• Does fund-raising
• Builds relationships with donors

SKILLS
• Listening skills
• Organizational skills
• Leadership

SALARY
$30,000–$60,000

MEANINGFUL PART OF THE JOB
"Students in our programs don't all become artists. But they all learn skills that last a lifetime."

CAREER CONNECTION
Education & Training
www.careerclusters.org

Related Jobs
• dance teacher
• principal
• artist

Focus Skills | Solve Problems | Ask Questions

What should a tour of your school include?

You are a guide for new students at your school. Plan a school tour. Then work with a partner to role-play a tour of your school.

❶ **Solve Problems.** Think back to your first day at your school. What do you wish you had known? List questions a new student might have.

A. _____

B. _____

C. _____

❷ **Identify important places and people.** Choose five important places and people in your school that new students need to know.

Places

A. _____   D. _____

_____   _____

B. _____   E. _____

_____   _____

C. _____

_____

People

Principal: _____   Counselor: _____

Friendly teachers: _____   Other important people: _____

_____   _____

❸ **Describe school activities.** What happens at lunch and recess? What teams and after-school programs are available?

A. _____

_____

B. _____

_____

C. _____

_____

④ **Do a role-play.** Decide who will play the new student and who will be the school guide. Complete the card for your role.

NEW STUDENT: _____
NAME

List five questions you might have as a new student.

1. _____
_____

2. _____
_____

3. _____
_____

4. _____
_____

5. _____
_____

SCHOOL GUIDE: _____
NAME

Write three sentences to introduce your school. What is your school like? What should new students know right away?

_____
_____
_____
_____
_____

⑤ **Now, act it out!** Take turns asking and answering questions. If you are the new student, ask lots of questions! If you are the guide, try to be as helpful as you can.

Comprehension

▶ **Fill in the circle next to the correct answer.**

1. When Jair Saenz first moved to America, he couldn't understand the _____.
   Ⓐ temperature
   Ⓑ time
   Ⓒ language
   Ⓓ holidays

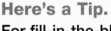

Here's a Tip.
For fill-in-the-blank questions, substitute each answer for the blank in the sentence. Then pick the best one.

2. Why did Virpal move to America?
   Ⓐ She was moving to be with her older sister.
   Ⓑ She was moving to be with her mother.
   Ⓒ She was moving to get away from her family.
   Ⓓ She wanted to learn a new language.

3. What happened to Virpal during her journey to the U.S.?
   Ⓐ She was stopped by a guard in a European airport.
   Ⓑ She was met by her mom in a European airport.
   Ⓒ She moved to Canada for five years.
   Ⓓ Her mom came to meet her in India.

CRITICAL READING

4. **Synthesize:** Which did Hispanic Americans bring to the United States?
   Ⓐ salsa and burritos
   Ⓑ jazz and blues
   Ⓒ sushi and dumplings
   Ⓓ pizza and french fries

CRITICAL READING

5. **Synthesize:** Many new immigrants to the U.S. need to _____.
   Ⓐ play soccer
   Ⓑ visit other countries
   Ⓒ learn English
   Ⓓ learn Spanish

Vocabulary

▶ **Fill in the circle next to the correct definition for each underlined word.**

1. China is on the other side of the globe from the United States.

   Ⓐ country   Ⓒ society

   Ⓑ attitude   Ⓓ world

2. Americans have the liberty to voice their opinions.

   Ⓐ freedom   Ⓒ slavery

   Ⓑ money   Ⓓ knowledge

3. Do you know the fastest route to school from your home?

   Ⓐ car   Ⓒ way to get somewhere

   Ⓑ bus line   Ⓓ time on a clock

▶ **Choose the antonym for the underlined word.**

4. The scientist achieved his goal of finding a cure for the disease.

   Ⓐ won   Ⓒ failed

   Ⓑ accomplished   Ⓓ found

▶ **Choose the synonym for the underlined word.**

5. Virpal's journey from India to the United States was very long.

   Ⓐ airplane   Ⓒ trip

   Ⓑ luggage   Ⓓ walk

Short Answer

CRITICAL READING

▶ **Synthesize: Use what you've learned in this Workshop to answer the question below. Check your spelling and grammar.**

If you were new to America, what might you find difficult to get used to? Why?

_____

_____

_____

_____

WORKSHOP 3

COMPREHENSION FOCUS
Story Elements

CRITICAL READING FOCUS
Evaluate

Reading Bud's Breakfast I **Historical Fiction**

Literary Text

BUD, NOT BUDDY

Christopher Paul Curtis had a big secret. He was working in a car factory . . . but he really wanted to be a writer. He started working on a book. Finally, he finished it. Kids loved it.

Now, Curtis writes full time. "If I knew writing was this much fun," he says, "I would have started when I was four."

Curtis's second book is *Bud, Not Buddy*. Bud is a young boy on his own. He is looking for his father. Often he is poor and hungry. Bud's sense of humor gets him through a lot of hard times. But now and then he needs a little extra help.

Academic Vocabulary

Target Word ⊙	Meaning	Examples
▶ Read the Target Words. Rate each one using the scale below.*	▶ Read the Target Word meanings. Write in the missing words.	▶ Finish the Target Word examples below.
privilege (p. 66) *priv•i•lege* (noun) ① ② ③ ④	a special _____ or advantage	• It is a **privilege** to _____ _____ • _____ _____ is a **privilege** we may get in school.
improve (p. 66) *im•prove* (verb) ① ② ③ ④	to make or get _____	If I practice, my skateboarding skills will **improve**.
grateful (p. 70) *grate•ful* (adjective) ① ② ③ ④	thankful	• I'm **grateful** _____ _____ • When I _____, my friend was **grateful**.
patient (p. 74) *pa•tient* (adjective) ① ② ③ ④	able to _____ for a _____ time	• I try to be **patient** with _____ _____ • The music teacher is very **patient** with _____
available (p. 74) *a•vail•a•ble* (adjective) ① ② ③ ④	possible to get	• I like to _____ _____ when free time is **available**. • Are _____ still **available**?

*Rating Scale
① = I don't know the word.   **③** = I think I know the word.
② = I've seen it or heard it.   **④** = I know it and use it.

Comprehension Focus

Story Elements

A **novel** is a book that tells a story about made-up characters and events. "Bud's Breakfast" is part of the novel *Bud, Not Buddy*. The novel is historical fiction, which means it is set in the past. To understand a story, look for these elements:

1. **Setting** is where and when a story takes place. This story takes place in Flint, Michigan, during the Great Depression of the 1930s. It was a time when many people were poor and hungry, and they went to the mission for food.

2. **Characters** are the people in the story. The main character is the most important character. These are the characters in this story:

**Bud,
a 10-year-old boy**

**the man at
the mission**

**Bud's
"pretend family"**

3. **Plot** is the sequence of events in a story. The plot contains a problem that the main character needs to solve. In "Bud's Breakfast," Bud is a 10-year-old boy living on his own. He is hungry and needs to eat. When Bud gets turned away from a food line at a mission, he's got a big problem. Will Bud go hungry?

4. **Theme** is an important message about life that the author wants readers to understand. One theme in this story is: When times are tough, some people are mean and others are kind.

▶ **Turn the page to begin reading Bud's story.**

Bud's Breakfast

▶ **Complete this chart as you reread the story.**

	Part 1 (pp. 64–67)	Part 2 (pp. 68–71)	Part 3 (pp. 72–75)
Setting	Time: one morning the 1930s Place: Flint, Michigan	Time: Place:	Time: Place:
Character	Who is the main character? Describe him/her:	How does the character change?	What is the character like now?
Plot	What happens at the beginning of the story?	What happens in the middle of the story?	How does the story end?
Theme	Author's message:		

Active Reading

★**STAR** What does the man at the mission tell Bud?

VOCABULARY
Target Word

farther

far•ther (adverb)

Rate It: ① ② ③ ④

Meaning

at a _____

than something else

Example

_____ is **farther** from

my school than _____ is.

Craft and Structure

Point of View This story is told from the **first-person point of view**. The narrator is a character who tells the story using the words *I* and *we*.

▶ **WRITE** Which character is telling this story?

_____

_____

React and Write

▶ **WRITE** Bud is hungry, but the man tries to send him away. What would you do if you were Bud?

Bud's Breakfast

by Christopher Paul Curtis

UH-OH. My eyes opened and I could see the sun behind the branch of a Christmas tree.

I jumped up, folded my blanket inside my suitcase, hid it, and started running the six or seven blocks down to the mission.

I turned the corner and said, "Whew!" There were still people lined up waiting. I started walking along the line. The end was a lot **farther** away than I thought. The line turned all the way

Words to Know!	**mission** a church or other place where aid is given to people in need

Story Elements

Setting

1. **CIRCLE** As the story begins, Bud has been sleeping outside. Mark a detail that shows this.

Character

2. ▶ **WRITE** How do you think Bud feels when he hears that the food line is closed?

_____

_____

_____

Plot

3. ▶ **WRITE** What problem does Bud have?

_____

_____

_____

Theme

4. ✔ **CHECK** A theme of this story is: When times are tough, some people are mean and others are kind.

What event on page 65 shows that people can be mean when times are tough?

around two corners, then crossed over one street before I saw the last person. Shucks. I walked up to get behind him.

He said, "Line's closed. These here folks are the last ones." He pointed at a man standing next to a woman who was carrying a baby.

I said, "But sir . . ."

He said, "But nothing. Line's closed. These here folks are the last ones." ➤

Active Reading

★STAR What does the man take out of his pocket?

VOCABULARY
Target Word

expect

ex•pect (verb)

Rate It: ① ② ③ ④

Meaning

to _____ that

something _____

Example

I **expect** to _____

_____ after school today.

Craft and Structure

Plot Device: Suspense is the curiosity readers feel when they wonder what will happen. Authors build suspense to give a story interest.

▶ **WRITE** Why does suspense build when the man walks toward Bud?

_____

_____

_____

React and Write

▶ **WRITE** What might Bud be thinking when someone puts a hand on his neck?

It was time to start lying. If I didn't get any food now I'd have to steal something out of someone's garbage. Or I wouldn't be able to eat until the mission opened for supper.

I said, "Sir, I—"

The man raised his hand and said, "Look, kid, everybody's got a story. And everybody knows the rules. The line closes at seven o'clock. How's it fair to these people who been here since five o'clock that you can sleep until"—he looked at his wristwatch—"until seven-fifteen? Then you come busting down here **expecting** to eat? You think you got some kind of special privilege just 'cause you're skinny and raggedy? Look in the line. There's lots of folks look just like you. You ain't the worst."

"Supper starts at six p.m., but you see how things is. If you plan on getting fed you better be in line by four. Now get out of here before I get rough with you."

Shucks, being hungry for a whole day is about as bad as it can get. I said, "But . . ."

He reached in his pocket and pulled something out that looked like a heavy black strap. He slapped it across his hand. Uh-oh, here we go again.

He said, "That's it, no more talk. You opened your mouth one time too many. You rotten kids today don't listen to no one. But I'ma show you something that'll improve your hearing." He slapped the strap on his hand and started walking toward me.

Words to Know!	**raggedy**	torn and in bad condition

I was wrong when I said being hungry for a day is about as bad as it can get. Being hungry plus having a big knot on your head from a black leather strap would be even worse.

I backed away. But I only got two steps before I felt a giant warm hand wrap around my neck from behind. I looked up to see whose doggone hand was so doggone big and why they'd put it around my neck. ➤

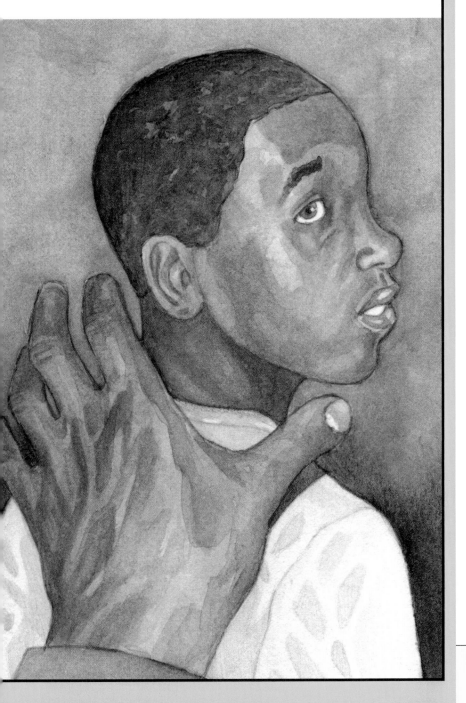

Story Elements

Setting

1. (CIRCLE) What time does the breakfast line at the mission close? What time does Bud arrive?

Character

2. UNDERLINE Mark two words that describe Bud.

Plot

3. ▮➤ WRITE Does it seem like Bud's problem is getting better or worse? Explain.

_____

_____

_____

_____

_____

_____

Theme

4. ✔CHECK A theme of this story is: When times are tough, some people are mean and others are kind.

Mark a word that Bud uses to describe the hand on his neck. This word gives readers a clue about whether the person holding his neck will be mean or kind.

➤ Now go to page 63. Add details to Part 1 of the chart.

Active Reading

★**STAR** What does the tall man in overalls call Bud?

CRITICAL READING

Evaluate

▶ **WRITE** The man pretends that Bud is his son so that Bud can eat. Do you think it is fair for the man to do this? Why or why not?

_____

_____

_____

_____

_____

_____

Craft and Structure

Point of View The **first-person point of view** allows the narrator to share his or her own thoughts and feelings while telling the story.

CIRCLE Mark two places where Bud shares his thoughts or feelings about what happens in the story.

React and Write

▶ **WRITE** If you were Bud, would you trust this family? Why or why not?

A very tall, square-shaped man in old blue overalls looked down at me. He said, "Clarence, what took you so long?"

I got ready to say, "My name's not Clarence. And please don't choke me, sir. I'll leave." But as soon as I opened my mouth he gave my head a shake. He said, "I told you to hurry back, now where you been?" He gave me a shove and said, "Get back in line with your momma."

I looked up and down the line to see who was supposed to be my momma. Then a woman pointed her finger at her feet and said, "Clarence, you get over here right now." There were two little kids hanging on to her skirt.

I walked over to where she was. And she gave me a good hard smack on the head. Shucks, for someone who was just pretending to be my momma she sure did slap me a good one. ➤

Story Elements

Setting

1. ▶ **WRITE** Where does Bud join the family who calls him Clarence?

_____

_____

_____

Character

2. **UNDERLINE** What does the momma of the family do when Bud reaches her?

Plot

3. ▶ **WRITE** What happens in this part of the story?

_____

_____

_____

Theme

4. ▶ **WRITE** A theme of this story is: When times are tough, some people are mean and others are kind. How do the two men in the story show this?

_____

_____

_____

_____

Active Reading

★**STAR** What do the people in line think when Bud cuts in front of them?

VOCABULARY
Target Word

credit

cred•it (noun)

Rate It: ③ ④

Meaning

approval or _____

for doing something

Example

Lisa deserves **credit** for _____

_____

Craft and Structure

Figurative Language: Simile
A simile compares two things that are not alike, using the words *like* or *as*. Example: *The hot air was like a dragon's breath.*

UNDERLINE the simile that Bud uses to describe the sudden change in mood when people in line finally see the mission door.

React and Write

▶ **WRITE** If you were poor and hungry, what might you think of the sign hanging over the mission?

I said, "Ow!"

The big square man who'd grabbed my neck looked at the man with the strap. He said, "Boy had to go use the crapper. Told him not to waste time. But like you said, these kids today don't listen to nobody."

The strap man looked at the size of the man who called me Clarence. Then he walked back to the end of the line.

When the overall man got back in line I said, "Thank you, sir, I really tried to get—" But *he* popped me in the back of the head, hard, and said, "Next time don't be gone so long."

The two little kids busted out laughing and said, "Nyah-nyah-nyah-nyah-nyah, Clarence got a lickin', Clarence got a lickin'."

I told them, "Shut up, and don't call me—" Then *both* my pretend poppa and my pretend momma smacked my head.

She looked at the people directly behind us and said, "Mercy, when they get to be this age . . ."

The people weren't too happy about me taking cuts in the line. But when they looked at how big my pretend daddy was and they saw how hard him and my pretend momma were going upside my head they decided they wouldn't say anything.

I was grateful to these people. But I wished they'd quit popping me in the head. And it seems like with all the names in the world they could've come up with a better one for me than Clarence.

I stood in line with my pretend family for a long, long time. Everybody was very quiet about standing in line, even my pretend brother and sister and all the other kids. When we finally got around the last

corner and could see the door and folks going in, it seemed like a bubble busted. People started laughing and talking. The main thing people were talking about was the great big sign hanging over the building.

It showed a gigantic picture of a family of four rich white people sitting in a car and driving somewhere. You could tell it was a family 'cause they all looked exactly alike. The only difference was that the daddy had a big head and a hat. The momma had the same head with a woman's hat. The girl had two big yellow pigtails coming out from above her ears. They all had big shiny teeth and big shiny eyes and big shiny cheeks and big shiny smiles. Shucks, you'd need to squint your eyes if that shiny family drove anywhere near you.

You could tell they were rich 'cause the car looked like it had room for eight or nine more people in it. They had movie star clothes on. The woman was wearing a coat with a hunk of fur around the neck. The man was wearing a suit and a tie. And the kids looked like they were wearing ten-dollar-apiece jackets.

Writ about their car in fancy letters it said, THERE'S NO PLACE LIKE AMERICA TODAY!

My pretend daddy read it and said, "Uh-uh-uh, well, you got to give them **credit**. You wouldn't expect that they'd have the nerve to come down here and tell the truth." ➤

| **Words to Know!** | **nerve** | courage |

Story Elements

Setting

1. (CIRCLE) What do the people in line see and talk about?

Character

2. ▷ **WRITE** How might Bud feel during this part of the story?

_____

_____

Plot

3. ▷ **WRITE** How does the family help with Bud's problem?

_____

_____

_____

▶ Now go to page 63. Add details to Part 2 of the chart.

CRITICAL READING
Evaluate

▷ **WRITE** Does Bud's "pretend daddy" like the sign over the building? Why or why not?

_____

_____

_____

_____

Active Reading

★**STAR** What does the mission serve for breakfast?

 VOCABULARY
Target Word

worth

worth (adjective)

Rate It: ① ② ③ ④

Meaning

useful, desirable, or _____

_____ to do

Example

Dad says _____

_____ is **worth**

the effort.

CRITICAL READING
Evaluate

▶ **WRITE** How do you think the oatmeal will taste to Bud? Explain.

_____

_____

_____

React and Write

▶ **WRITE** What does this part of the story tell you about how hungry people were during the Great Depression?

When we finally got into the building it was **worth** the wait. The first thing you noticed when you got inside was how big the place was, and how many people were in it and how quiet it was. The only sound you could hear was when someone scraped a spoon across the bottom of their bowl or pulled a chair in or put one back. Or when the people in front of you dragged their feet on the floor moving up to where they were spooning out the food.

Words to Know!	**scraped** scratched

After we'd picked up our spoons and bowls a lady dug a big mess of oatmeal out of a giant pot. She swopped it down into our bowls. She smiled and said, "I hope you enjoy."

Me and my pretend family all said, "Thank you, ma'am." Then a man put two pieces of bread and an apple and a big glass of milk on your tray. He said, "Please read the signs to your children. Thank you." ➤

Story Elements

Setting

1. **CIRCLE** What is the inside of the mission like? Mark three details that describe it.

Character

2. ▶ **WRITE** How does Bud look in the illustration? Why do you think he looks this way?

_____

_____

Plot

3. ▶ **WRITE** How has Bud's problem been solved?

_____

_____

Theme

4. ▶ **WRITE** A theme of this story is: When times are tough, some people are mean and others are kind.

   Is the lady with the oatmeal mean or nice? Explain your response.

_____

_____

Read for Detail

✔ **CHECK** Identify three sounds that Bud hears inside the mission.

Active Reading

★**STAR** What does Bud ask his "pretend family" after they finish eating?

VOCABULARY
Target Word

normally

nor•mal•ly (adverb)

Rate It: ① ② ③ ④

Meaning

often, or _____

Example

On the weekends, I **normally**

_____

_____

React and Write

▶**WRITE** Do you like Bud? Would you want to be his friend? Explain why or why not.

Make Inferences

1. Do you think that Bud can read? How do you know?

2. Why do you think that the man pretending to be Bud's daddy reads the signs for his children?

We all said, "Thank you, sir." Then we walked past some signs someone'd stuck up on the wall.

One said, PLEASE DO NOT SMOKE. Another said, PLEASE EAT AS QUICKLY AND QUIETLY AS POSSIBLE. Another one said, PLEASE BE CONSIDERATE AND PATIENT—CLEAN UP AFTER YOURSELF— YOUR NEIGHBORS WILL BE EATING AFTER YOU. And the last one said, WE ARE TERRIBLY SORRY BUT WE HAVE NO WORK AVAILABLE.

My pretend daddy read the signs to my pretend brother and sister. We all sat at a long table with strangers on both sides of us.

The oatmeal was delicious! I poured some of my milk into it so it wouldn't be so lumpy and mixed it all together.

My pretend mother opened her pocketbook. She took out a little brown envelope. She reached inside of it and sprinkled something on my pretend brother's and sister's oatmeal. Then she said to them, "I know that's not as much as you **normally** get. But I wanted to ask you if you minded sharing some with Clarence."

They pouted and gave me a couple of dirty looks. My pretend mother said, "Good." She emptied the rest of the envelope over my oatmeal. Brown sugar!

Shucks, I didn't even mind them calling me Clarence anymore. I said, "Thank you, Momma, ma'am."

She and my pretend daddy laughed. And he said, "It took you long enough to catch on, Clarence." He acted like he was going to smack me again, but he didn't.

After we'd finished all our food, we put our bowls up. And I thanked my pretend family again. I asked them, "Are you going to be coming back for supper?"

My pretend momma said, "No, dear, we only come here mornings. But you make sure you get here plenty early, you hear?"

I said, "Yes, Momma, I mean, ma'am."

I watched them walking away. My pretend brother looked back at me and stuck out his tongue. Then he reached up and took my pretend mother's hand. I couldn't really blame him. I don't think I'd be real happy about sharing my brown sugar and my folks with any strange kids either. END

Words to Know! | **considerate** thoughtful

Meet the Author

CHRISTOPHER PAUL CURTIS
Born: May 10, 1953 in Flint, Michigan

Awards: The novel *Bud, Not Buddy* received the Newbery Medal and the Coretta Scott King Award. Curtis's other books have won the Newbery Honor, the Coretta Scott King Honor, and many other prizes.

Themes: Curtis often writes about racism, family, love, and hope.

 Story Elements

Character

1. ▶ **WRITE** How does Bud feel about what his "pretend brother" does as they part?

_____

_____

_____

Plot

2. ▶ **WRITE** How does the story end?

_____

_____

_____

▶ Now go to page 63. Complete Part 3 of the chart.

✓ Skills Check

1. **UNDERLINE** What advice does the mother give to Bud?

2. ▶ **WRITE** How does the family help Bud?

_____

_____

WORD CHALLENGE

START

1 **Choose one.** Which would you like to have **available** for free?

- [ ] doctor visits
- [ ] Internet access
- [ ] bus and train rides

3 **Check them.** Which would make you feel **grateful**?

- [ ] You forget your lunch. Your friends share theirs.
- [ ] Your brother wears your new sneakers to paint his bedroom.
- [ ] Your friend breaks a window. She says you did it.
- [ ] Your bike gets a flat tire. Your sister patches it.

2 HOMOPHONES

Homophones are words that sound alike but have different meanings and spellings. Examples are *piece* and *peace* or *wait* and *weight*.

Match each word to its homophone.

bear	by	rode

Homophone

buy: _____

road: _____

bare: _____

Complete the sentence with two homophones. (Hint: One is a color.)

The wind _____ my

new _____ shirt right off the clothesline.

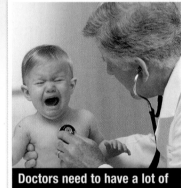

Doctors need to have a lot of patience with their patients.

4 **Think about it.** When is it hardest for you to be **patient**? Rank these situations from 1 to 4.

1 = hardest to be **patient**
4 = easiest to be **patient**

____ waiting in line for your favorite roller coaster

____ waiting in the school lunch line

____ waiting for a shot at the doctor's office

____ waiting for a pizza delivery

5 **Decide.** Read each choice. Write *P* if you consider it a **privilege**. Write *NP* if it is not a **privilege** for you.

____ staying up late

____ taking music lessons

____ going to the movies

____ taking out the trash

____ getting an allowance

____ starring in the class play

6 **Rank them.** What should earn you the most **credit**? Rank these choices from 0 to 3.

0 = no **credit**!   3 = a lot of **credit**!

____ **credit** for messing up your room

____ **credit** for getting a good grade on a quiz

____ **credit** for forgetting your homework

____ **credit** for arriving at school on time all year

7 **Mark them.** How would you **improve** your school? Pick one or more.

☐ add new books to the library

☐ serve healthier food in the lunchroom

☐ make the school day longer

Now, add your own idea:

_____

_____

8 **WORD FAMILIES**

Normally, I'm **normal**. But today I'm WEIRD!

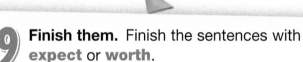

A **word family** is a group of words that share the same base word and have related meanings, such as *normal*, *normally*, and *abnormal*. *Normal* means "usual" or "expected." *Normally* means "usually." *Abnormal* means "unusual" or "not normal."

Complete each sentence with *normal*, *normally*, or *abnormal*.

1. Carlos doesn't _____ sleep late, but today he slept until noon.

2. His _____ wake-up time is 7:00 A.M.

3. It is _____ for Carlos to sleep later than 7:00 A.M.

9 **Finish them.** Finish the sentences with **expect** or **worth**.

Playing the drums is so fun. Of course, you can't _____ to play well right away. It takes a lot of practice. But in the end, the hard work is _____ it.

10 **Circle them.** Which is **farther** from where you live?

Your school **OR** the nearest park?

The grocery store **OR** the post office?

The movie theater **OR** your best friend's house?

Writing Text Type
Literary Analysis

In a **literary analysis**, the writer discusses the characters, plot, or setting of a story.

▶ Read Latisha Small's literary analysis of the setting of "Bud's Breakfast."

Topic Sentence

A **topic sentence** identifies the story's text type, title, and author.

1. UNDERLINE the **topic sentence**.

The topic sentence includes a **controlling idea** about the story's characters, plot, or setting.

2. BOX the **controlling idea**.

Detail Sentences

Detail sentences give supporting **details** and **examples**.

3. ✔ CHECK three **details, quotations,** or **examples**.

Direct quotations support the writer's ideas about the story.

4. DOUBLE UNDERLINE two **direct quotations**.

Language Use

Linking words and phrases introduce and connect ideas.

5. CIRCLE two **linking words or phrases**.

Concluding Sentence

The **concluding sentence** sums up the writer's ideas.

6. ★ STAR the **concluding sentence**.

Student Model

Hard Times for Bud and Others
by Latisha Small

"Bud's Breakfast" by Christopher Paul Curtis is a historical fiction story set during the Great Depression, when many people were poor and hungry. In this story, a boy named Bud is alone in the world. When Bud tries to get breakfast, a man tells him, "Line's closed." (65) In fact, the man even threatens to beat Bud. "Shucks, being hungry . . . is about as bad as it can get . . . [but] being hungry plus having a big knot on your head . . . would be even worse," Bud thinks. (66, 67) Bud's story shows how difficult life was during the Great Depression, even for children. In conclusion, the harsh setting of this story shows that life was a struggle for Bud and others who lived during this difficult time.

B *I* U

P 1

Brainstorm

▶ Read the writing prompt. Then use the idea web to brainstorm writing ideas.

Plot

Setting

Writing Prompt:
Analyze the characters,
plot, or setting in the story
"Bud's Breakfast."

Character

Choose Your Topic

▶ Select one of your ideas from the idea web. Then complete this sentence.

I plan to write about _____

because _____

_____

Organize Ideas for Writing

▶ **Complete this outline with notes for your literary analysis.**

I. Topic Sentence. State your idea about the story's characters, plot, or setting.

Topic: _____

Controlling Idea: _____

II. Detail Sentences. List supporting details, examples, and quotations.

Detail 1: _____

Detail 2: _____

III. Concluding Sentence. Sum up your ideas about the story. _____

_____

Write Your Draft

▶ **Write a draft of your literary analysis.**

Writing Prompt:
Analyze the characters, plot, or setting in "Bud's Breakfast."

WORD CHOICES	
Everyday	**Precise**
mean	cruel, cold
nice	kind, considerate
ask	plead, convince

_____
(title)

▶ **Write your topic sentence.**

Topic Sentence

In the historical fiction story "Bud's Breakfast" by Christopher Paul Curtis,

_____.
(controlling idea)

▶ **Type your topic sentence on the computer or write it on paper. Then use these linking words and phrases to complete a draft of your paragraph.**

Detail Sentences

For example, . . .	Another example . . .
In addition, . . .	Instead, . . .

Concluding Sentence

In conclusion, . . .	To sum up the story, . . .

Revise Your Paragraph

▶ **Evaluate:** Rate your literary analysis. Then have a writing partner rate it.

Scoring Guide

needs improvement	average	good	excellent
1	2	3	4

1. **UNDERLINE** the topic sentence. Does it state the story's text type, title, and author?
   Self   1   2   3   4
   Partner 1   2   3   4

2. **BOX** the controlling idea. Does it make a point about the story's characters, plot, or setting?
   Self   1   2   3   4
   Partner 1   2   3   4

3. ✔ **CHECK** details, quotations, and examples from the story. Do they support the writer's ideas?
   Self   1   2   3   4
   Partner 1   2   3   4

4. **CIRCLE** linking words and phrases. Do they connect ideas?
   Self   1   2   3   4
   Partner 1   2   3   4

5. **DOUBLE UNDERLINE** quotations. Do they support the writer's ideas?
   Self   1   2   3   4
   Partner 1   2   3   4

6. ★**STAR** the concluding sentence. Does it sum up the writer's ideas?
   Self   1   2   3   4
   Partner 1   2   3   4

▶ **Discuss:** Give feedback on your partner's literary analysis.

1. Start with a positive comment about your partner's literary analysis.

You did an effective job of _____

_____

You made an interesting point about

_____

2. Give your partner suggestions for revision.

Body sentences should include _____

_____

Your analysis would be stronger if you

_____

_____

3. Answer any questions your partner has about your suggestions.

4. Ask your partner for feedback. Use the frames below to summarize your partner's feedback.

I did an effective job of . . .
I made an interesting point about . . .
Body sentences should include . . .
My analysis would be stronger if . . .

▶ **Revise:** Now revise your literary analysis.

Grammar CORRECTING RUN-ON SENTENCES

A **run-on sentence** is made up of two complete thoughts that are incorrectly joined together.

- To fix a run-on sentence, separate the ideas into two **complete sentences**.
- Or, insert a comma and a connecting word between the thoughts.

Examples	
Run-on sentence:	Bud woke up late he ran to get in line.
Complete sentences:	Bud woke up late. He ran to get in line.
Complete sentence:	Bud woke up late, so he ran to get in line.

▶ **Put an R next to each run-on sentence. Put a *C* next to each complete sentence.**

1. Bud walked along the line it went around two corners. R

2. Bud was hungry he decided to tell a lie. _____

3. The man pulled out a strap, and Bud was scared. _____

4. A tall man grabbed Bud he shook him. _____

5. A woman pointed to her feet two kids stood by her. _____

6. Bud was grateful, but he didn't like being slapped. _____

▶ **Rewrite the run-on sentences below as complete sentences.**

7. A lady was serving oatmeal she put some into Bud's bowl.

_____

_____

8. They ate oatmeal the kids got brown sugar, too.

_____

_____

9. The man laughed he thought Bud was funny.

_____

_____

10. The boy stuck out his tongue Bud did not mind.

_____

_____

▶ **Edit Your Draft.** Reread your draft. **Are there any run-on sentences?** If so, fix them.

Usage USING CORRECT WORD ORDER

The **order of words** in a sentence must make sense.

- An adjective comes before the noun it describes.
- A helping verb comes just before the main verb in a statement.

Examples

Correct	Incorrect
Bud was a funny kid.	Bud was a kid funny.
Bud liked what he was eating.	Bud liked what was he eating.

▶ **Find and correct five errors in this paragraph.**

Student Model

> I thought "Bud's Breakfast" was a story weak. To start with, I did not like Bud. He should have been more pashent with the people in the breakfast line. Also, Bud not was greatful for his pretend family's help. Finally, I think that the family should have let Bud live with them then Bud's life would have been easier. I do not recommend this boring story.

CHECK AND CORRECT

- ☐ **UNDERLINE** two word order errors and correct them.
- ☐ Correct one run-on sentence.
- ☐ **CIRCLE** two spelling errors and correct them.

▶ **Edit Your Draft.** Look at the sentences in your draft. **Do they all use correct word order?** Fix any that do not.

Final Draft/Present

▶ Write a final draft of your paragraph on the computer or on paper. Recheck it and correct any errors before you present it.

Evaluate an Author Home Page

Many authors have websites that tell about their work and their lives. This is the home page for author Charles R. Smith Jr.'s website.

▶ **Read the home page and answer the questions.**

MARK IT

- **CIRCLE** the URL (web address) for this website.
- ✔ **CHECK** the link to the author's contact information.
- ★ **STAR** a photo of the author.

http://www.charlesrsmithjr.com/

HOME
ABOUT ME
MY BOOKS
ACTIVITIES
SCHOOL VISITS
CONTACT ME

WELCOME!

Hello, and welcome to my site! I'm Charles R. Smith Jr. I take pictures and write children's books. Maybe you have heard of my books about basketball.

I try to make my site as fun and informative as possible, so hunt around! **Want to play a game? Click on the basketball at the top of the page and see if you can get it in the basket!**

As more of my books come out and more projects come along, I will add more to the site for you.

Each time you return, check out the **What's New** links on the right. Enjoy!

WHAT'S NEW?

My People
2010 Winner, Coretta Scott King Award for Illustration!

I created images of many faces to illustrate a powerful poem by **Langston Hughes**. My goal was to show the wide diversity of people in black culture.

Chameleon
The wait is over! My first novel is here! It tells the story of Shawn and three friends in Compton, California, the summer before high school.

❶ **Which is the best link to click to find out more about this author's books?**

   Ⓐ My Books   Ⓒ About Me
   Ⓑ Activities   Ⓓ Contact Me

❷ **Which part of this home page is likely to change most often?**

   Ⓐ Welcome!   Ⓒ What's New?
   Ⓑ Basketball game   Ⓓ Author name

❸ **Why do you think that Charles has a basketball game on his home page?**

_____

_____

_____

_____

_____

Author and Illustrator
Charles R. Smith Jr.

This popular author writes and illustrates award-winning books for young readers.

▶ **Read the interview and job information. Then answer the questions about Charles R. Smith Jr.'s work.**

S Scholastic: Who was a mentor to you in your career?

Charles R. Smith Jr.: After I published my first book, I met the children's book author and illustrator James Ransome. A few years later, I was ready to branch out in different directions with my books. James helped me to find an agent who worked on selling my new book ideas.

S What kind of person makes a good writer or illustrator?

You need to be creative and finish what you start. You have to be able to deal with criticism as well as praise.

S When you research topics for nonfiction books, how do you decide what to include?

I look for information that would be interesting to kids. In my book about Muhammad Ali and Jack Johnson, two boxers, I wanted to know when and why they got interested in boxing.

❶ How did a mentor help Charles?

_____

_____

❷ How important do you think it is to have a mentor? Mark the line.

👎 1   2   3   4   5 👍
Not very important   **Very important**

❸ It is/is not (circle one) **important to have a mentor because**

_____

ON THE JOB

LOCATION
Poughkeepsie, New York

EDUCATION
Bachelor's degree in Photography

RESPONSIBILITIES
- Thinks of ideas for books
- Completes books on deadline

SKILLS
- Ability to draw and write
- Ability to work independently

SALARY
Experienced writers make $30,000–$73,000.

HARDEST PART OF THE JOB
"Writing a book is like running a marathon. Sometimes you want to quit, but you know you have to finish it."

CAREER CONNECTION

Arts, A/V Technology and Communications
www.careerclusters.org

Related Jobs
- book editor
- advertising writer
- speech writer

Focus Skills Resolve Conflicts | Present Effectively

Will Bud ever find a family to live with?

Bud is a young boy who is alone in the world. Create a storyboard for a movie scene about how Bud finds a family to call his own.

1. **Brainstorm.** How could Bud become part of a family? Brainstorm two ideas.

   A. ______________________________

   ____

   B. ______________________________

   ____

2. **Resolve Conflicts.** Describe conflicts Bud could have as he joins a family as its newest member. How could he solve each conflict?

Conflict	Solution
A.	
B.	

3. **Collaborate.** Work together to decide which of your conflict/solution pairs would make the best movie. Circle your group's choice.

4. **Plan your movie.** How will you show what happens? A shot is a single section of film. What will you show in the three shots in your movie scene? Think about what Bud and other people will do and say.

Shot	Who speaks? What do they say? What do they do?
1	
2	
3	

⑤ Create your storyboard. Create three shots for your movie scene. Sketch pictures to show the action in each shot. Next to each shot, write what characters say.

SHOT 1

Character's Words

_____
_____
_____
_____
_____
_____

SHOT 2

Character's Words

_____
_____
_____
_____
_____
_____

SHOT 3

Character's Words

_____
_____
_____
_____
_____

Comprehension

▶ **Fill in the circle next to the correct answer.**

1. What is Bud's main problem in this story?
   Ⓐ He is hurt.
   Ⓑ He is hungry.
   Ⓒ He is lost.
   Ⓓ He is mad.

2. When does this story take place?
   Ⓐ in the present day
   Ⓑ far off in the distant future
   Ⓒ in the 1930s during the Great Depression
   Ⓓ in the time of the Civil War

> **Here's a Tip.**
> For short-answer questions, restate the question in your answer. This helps focus your answer.

3. Bud's pretend parents help him by _____.
   Ⓐ letting him get in line with them so he can get food
   Ⓑ telling him how to get food at another food line
   Ⓒ telling him he should have gotten there earlier
   Ⓓ giving him their oatmeal

CRITICAL READING
4. Evaluate: Which is Bud's best personal quality?
   Ⓐ honesty
   Ⓑ humor
   Ⓒ gracefulness
   Ⓓ gentleness

CRITICAL READING
5. Evaluate: Which would be the <u>fairest</u> thing for Bud to do if he wants to get food at the mission again?
   Ⓐ He should make friends with the man with the strap.
   Ⓑ He should get in line with the "pretend family" again.
   Ⓒ He should get in line with a new family.
   Ⓓ He should get to the mission in time, before the line closes.

Vocabulary

▶ **Fill in the circle next to the correct definition of the underlined words.**

1. Bud was <u>grateful</u> for the hot meal.
   - Ⓐ hungry
   - Ⓑ thankful
   - Ⓒ ready
   - Ⓓ happy

2. Will Bud's situation <u>improve</u>?
   - Ⓐ get better
   - Ⓑ get worse
   - Ⓒ get bigger
   - Ⓓ get smaller

3. There wasn't much food <u>available</u>, so having brown sugar was a <u>privilege</u>.
   - Ⓐ useless; refusal
   - Ⓑ edible; confusion
   - Ⓒ possible to get; special advantage
   - Ⓓ able to be cooked; serious crime

▶ **Choose the correct definition for the underlined homophone.**

4. I had to be <u>patient</u> until the school bell rang.
   - Ⓐ able to wait calmly
   - Ⓑ able to think of new ideas
   - Ⓒ a helpful person
   - Ⓓ a person treated by a doctor

▶ **Choose the correct word from the word family.**

5. The children _____ have brown sugar with their oatmeal.
   - Ⓐ normal
   - Ⓑ abnormal
   - Ⓒ normalize
   - Ⓓ normally

Short Answer

▶ **Evaluate: Use what you've read in this Workshop to answer the question. Check your spelling and grammar.**

CRITICAL READING

Do you think that Bud is a survivor? Explain why.

_____

_____

_____

_____

WORKSHOP 4

INFORMATIONAL TEXT

COMPREHENSION FOCUS
Summarize

CRITICAL READING FOCUS
Analyze
Synthesize

Reading 1 Stop All Bullies! | **Letter**

Reading 2 Girl Fight | **Magazine Article**

Reading 3 Bullying: Get the Facts | **Life Skills Feature**

BULLIES BEWARE

Hitting. Punching. Pushing. That's only some of what bullies do. They also tease, put down, and embarrass other kids.

Do you know how to handle a bully? In this Workshop, you'll learn how to spot a bully. You'll find out why bullies push others around. And you'll get tips on how you can fight back!

Academic Vocabulary

Target Word ▶ Read the Target Words. Rate each one using the scale below.*	Meaning ▶ Read the Target Word meanings. Write in the missing words.	Example ▶ Finish the Target Word examples below. Write in the missing ones.
unite (p. 92) u•nite (verb) ① ② ③ ④	to bring _____; to make _____	• My friends from three different schools **united** _____ _____ • Most students in our school are **united** in favor of _____
struggle (p. 94) strug•gle (noun) ① ② ③ ④	a difficult challenge	• It is a **struggle** to _____ when you are tired. • _____
convince (p. 96) con•vince (verb) ① ② ③ ④	to make someone _____ you	My friend **convinced** me to try in-line skating.
expert (p. 96) ex•pert (noun) ① ② ③ ④	someone with special _____ or _____	• A police officer is an **expert** in _____ • _____
pressure (p. 99) pres•sure (noun) ① ② ③ ④	strong influence, force, or persuasion	• Sometimes I feel **pressure** to _____ • **Pressure** helps when I'm _____

*Rating Scale ① = I don't know the word. ② = I've seen it or heard it. ③ = I think I know the word. ④ = I know it and use it.

Letter

The Key Idea

▶ **WRITE** What is this letter mostly about?

_____

_____

VOCABULARY
Target Word

insist

in•sist *(verb)*

Rate It: ① ② ③ ④

Meaning

to make a firm _____

for or about something

Example

I would **insist** that we stay

indoors if _____

_____

React and Write

▶ **WRITE** Is bullying a problem in your school? Give details and examples to support your response.

Summarize

In one or two sentences, summarize the problem that students describe in this letter. Include the topic and important details.

Stop All Bullies!

September 15, 2010

Dear Principal Martinez:

Bullying is a big problem at our school. Kids are scared and upset. We want to stop all bullies now.

Last week, there was a bad case of bullying in the cafeteria. A group of fifth graders bullied a third grader. They told him to eat mashed potatoes mixed with mustard. The third grader said no. However, the bullies **insisted**. Everybody else was too afraid to help.

In fact, most kids at our school are afraid of bullies. We talked to the kids in our class. Over half said they were scared of being bullied. They were also afraid to stand up to bullies.

Bullying is bad because it can affect a kid's whole life. The victims of bullies can't focus on their schoolwork. Sometimes they even stay home from school. Worst of all, some victims turn into bullies themselves.

For these reasons, we want to start an anti-bullying club. We are asking for your support. If we all unite against bullies, we can stop them for good.

Sincerely,

Melissa Wilson   *Derek Johnson*   *José Diego* ⟨END⟩

Words to Know! | **affect** to influence or change

Comprehension Focus
Summarize

A **summary** is a short statement that tells the most important ideas in a reading. To summarize:

• Find the topic of the reading.
• Look for the most important details about the topic.
• Restate the topic and important details in a short summary. Use your own words.

▶ **Complete this chart with the topic and important details in "Stop All Bullies!"**

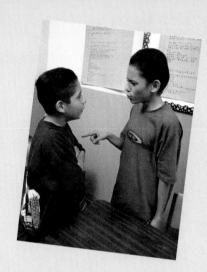

Topic

Details

1. A group of fifth graders forced a third grader to eat mashed potatoes mixed with mustard.

2.

3.

Summarize

▶ Now summarize the article. Check that you:

❏ state the topic.
❏ give important details.
❏ use your own words.

The Key Idea

▶ **WRITE** What is this magazine article mostly about?

_____

_____

VOCABULARY
Target Word

physical

phys•i•cal *(adjective)*

Rate It: ① ② ③ ④

Meaning

having to do with the _____

Example

The **physical** activity I most

enjoy is _____

_____

_____

React and Write

▶ **WRITE** You read about three girls who were bullied. Which girl do you think was hurt worst by bullying? Why?

GIRL FIGHT

HOW DO GIRLS FIGHT? MEET THREE GIRLS WHO WERE BULLIED—BY OTHER GIRLS.

by Grace Bromley

Just like boys, girls can be mean, tough bullies. But often, they don't get caught. That's because most girl bullies don't bully in obvious ways. Instead of throwing punches, girls may use words that hurt worse than any scratch or bruise.

WORDS HURT

Girl bullies often tease their victims about how they look. Bullies teased Keesha Washington because she wore glasses. Girls in Keesha's class called her names like Four-Eyes. For Keesha, just getting through class was a struggle.

Other girls make fun of their victims' families. Karen Williams had been a foster kid. Finally, she was adopted by a family. When Karen started sixth grade at her school, a popular girl bullied her. The bully laughed about Karen's home life. "She made

Do mean words hurt as much as punches?

fun of me because I was adopted," Karen says. "She was really mean. She picked on me because my mom and dad aren't my birth parents."

ALL ALONE

Girls who are bullied feel all alone. Often, no one talks to them or helps them out. All through middle school, kids called Kelsey Dodge names. They tried to make her cry. "If kids stuck up for me, they'd get bullied, too," she says.

Like Kelsey, most victims of teasing and name-calling have a tough time finding help. **Physical** bullying leaves marks you can see, like bruises. But no one can see the pain left by a bully's mean words. That's why girl bullies are hard to stop. ➤

Words to Know! **obvious** clear, easy to see

Summarize

1. ▯▶ **WRITE** What is the topic of "Words Hurt"?

_____

_____

2. **UNDERLINE** Mark two details in "Words Hurt" that tell about the topic.

3. Summarize "Words Hurt" in your own words to a partner.

4. ▯▶ **WRITE** What is the topic of "All Alone"?

_____

_____

5. **UNDERLINE** Identify two details in "All Alone" that tell about the topic.

6. Summarize "All Alone" in your own words to a partner.

CRITICAL READING
Synthesize

▶ **WRITE** How might things have been different for Kelsey if she had had a friend to talk to?

_____

_____

_____

Active Reading

★STAR Who says that she'll fight against bullying all her life?

 VOCABULARY
Target Word

nervous

ner•vous (adjective)

Rate It: ① ② ③ ④

Meaning

_____ or _____

_____ about something

Example

_____

_____

always makes me **nervous**.

React and Write

▶ **WRITE** Where would you go for help if you were bullied?

Summarize

In one or two sentences, summarize the topic and important details in "Bullies on the Run."

BULLIES ON THE RUN

How can you stop girls who bully? It's not easy. Keesha told her mom and her teachers about her bullies. Nothing happened at first. Then, the bullies got physical. They threw food at Keesha in the lunchroom. Finally, they were suspended.

Karen, the former foster child, also complained. She told her family and teachers about her bully. She convinced them to help her. In eighth grade, Karen and the bully were put in different classes.

Girl bullies can also get physical.

Kelsey never found help with her bullies. She had only one choice: waiting them out. Finally, in high school, the bullying stopped.

BAD MEMORIES

Keesha, Karen, and Kelsey have different stories. However, their bad memories are the same. They remember being bullied as the worst time of their lives. Experts say that many bullied kids feel this way.

Keesha still feels sad when she thinks about her bullies. Karen is always **nervous** at school. And Kelsey says that she'll fight against bullying all her life. "I know how it feels to get picked on," she says. "I'm never going to sit back and let someone else be treated the way they treated me." END

Words to Know!	**suspended**	forced to leave school temporarily

Comprehension Focus
Summarize

▶ **Complete this chart with the topic and important details in the article "Girl Fight."**

Topic

Details

1. _____

_____

2. _____

_____

3. _____

_____

Summarize

▶ **Now summarize the article. Check that you:**

❏ state the topic.
❏ give important details.
❏ use your own words.

💡 The Key Idea

▶ **WRITE** What is this life skills feature mostly about?

_____

_____

◎ VOCABULARY
Target Word

injure

in•jure (verb)

Rate It: ① ② ③ ④

Meaning

to _____ yourself

or someone else

Example

A _____ might **injure**

someone by _____

_____ him or her.

❗ React and Write

▶ **WRITE** Which is worse: hitting someone, or gossiping about a friend? Explain your response.

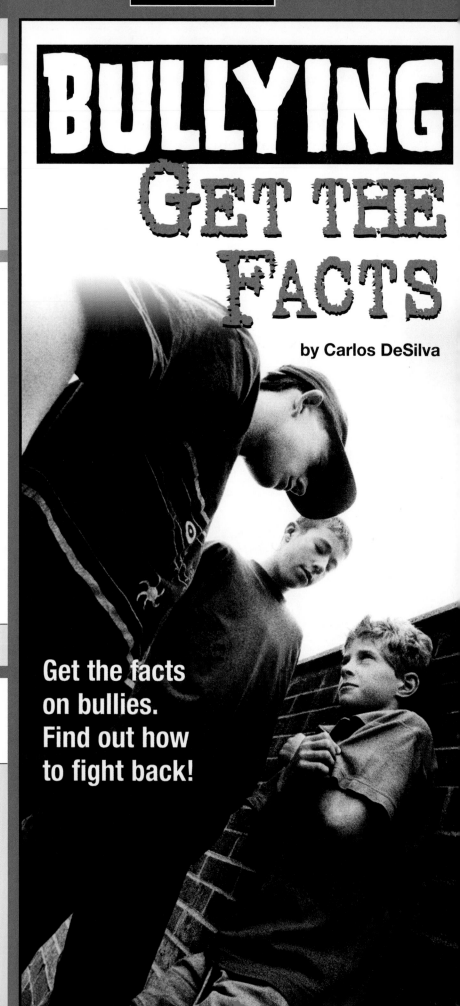

BULLYING
GET THE FACTS

by Carlos DeSilva

Get the facts
on bullies.
Find out how
to fight back!

How They Attack

There are three different kinds of bullying. But they all have one thing in common. They make kids feel sad, hurt, and alone.

Many bullies hit, push, or trip their victims. This is called physical bullying—and it really hurts! However, bullies don't always **injure** kids physically.

Another way to bully is with words. It's called verbal bullying. It includes name-calling and teasing. When verbal bullying happens on the Internet, it is called cyberbullying.

There's a third kind of bullying. It's called relationship bullying. It starts when friends bully a kid in their group. They spread gossip, leave the kid out, or put on the pressure to do something wrong.

Who Is a Bully?

Why do some kids become bullies? It may seem like they were just born mean. But kids become bullies for a lot of different reasons.

Some kids are picked on at home. At first, their older brothers and sisters pick on them. Sometimes their parents do, too. Later, at school, these kids become bullies themselves. They want to make others feel as bad as they do.

Other kids want attention. They want all eyes on them. They are convinced that they won't get enough attention by being good. So, they get it by being bad.

Finally, some kids are just spoiled! If your parents never teach you how to treat people, you might not know that bullying is wrong. Some parents think that their child is always right. Even when their child is a bully, the parents don't see it. ➤

Summarize

1. ▶ **WRITE** What is the topic of "How They Attack"?

_____

_____

2. **UNDERLINE** Mark three details that tell about the topic.

3. Summarize the section in your own words to a partner.

4. ▶ **WRITE** What is the topic of "Who Is a Bully?"

_____

_____

5. **UNDERLINE** Mark three details that tell about the topic.

6. Summarize the section in your own words to a partner.

REVIEW
Sequence of Events

⟨CIRCLE⟩ Mark three sequence words or phrases in "Who Is a Bully?"

CRITICAL READING
Analyze

▶ **WRITE** Pretend that a bully spreads mean rumors about a student, and tries to get other people to make fun of the student. What kind of bullying would this be?

_____

_____

💡 Active Reading

★**STAR** What percent of kids ages 12–15 feel pressure from bullies?

VOCABULARY
◎ Target Word

incident

in•ci•dent (noun)

Rate It: ① ② ③ ④

Meaning

something _____ or

_____ that happens

Example

An **incident** in the news that

I've heard a lot about is

_____

_____

❗ React and Write

▶**WRITE** How bad is bullying in your school? Tell about it.

🔲 Summarize

▶**WRITE** Summarize the topic and important details in the life skills feature "Bullying: Get the Facts."

The Bully's Victim

Who do bullies like to pick on? Most bullies look for easy targets. They want to feel powerful. They get a kick out of making kids cry. So they target kids who get upset and cry easily.

Bullies also pick on kids who don't look like everyone else. Their victims might be smaller or bigger than other kids. They might be kids who wear glasses or braces. Sometimes, bullies choose victims who belong to a different race or religion.

However, bullying can be a problem for all kids. Experts say that more than half of all kids ages 8–11 are worried about bullies. For older kids, the problem is even worse. Sixty-eight percent of kids ages 12–15 feel pressure from bullies. So, being a bully's victim is more common than you think.

Words to Know! | **abuse** harmful treatment of someone

📄 TEXT FEATURE Reading a Bar Graph

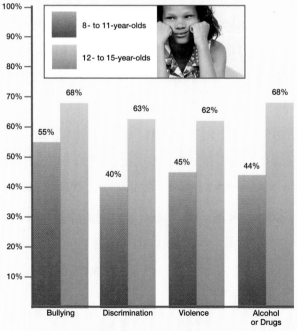

What Worries Kids

Legend: 8- to 11-year-olds / 12- to 15-year-olds

	Bullying	Discrimination	Violence	Alcohol or Drugs
8- to 11-year-olds	55%	40%	45%	44%
12- to 15-year-olds	68%	63%	62%	68%

SOURCE: KAISER FAMILY FOUNDATION

Fighting Back

What can you do to deal with a bully? There are many ways to fight back without fists. Check out these tips:

- **Control your emotions.** Bullies want to see you get upset. So, try not to let them see you cry. Walk away. Or, tell them to stop in a calm voice.

- **Help the victims.** If you see someone bullying someone else, try to stop it. Let victims know that they don't deserve the abuse. Kids with friends are less likely to get bullied.

- **Tell an adult.** Don't be afraid to tell an adult if you see a bullying **incident**. Your parents and teachers want you to be safe at school. Many schools have guidelines that protect victims. Know the rules—and be ready to fight back. _END_

A bar graph shows how information can be compared.

❶ What information does this double bar graph show?

Ⓐ the kinds of young people who fear bullies

Ⓑ the problems two groups of kids worry about

Ⓒ where bullied students live

Ⓓ the percentage of 8- to 11-year-olds and 12- to 15-year-olds who bully

❷ What color bar represents 8- to 11-year-olds?

Ⓐ green   Ⓒ yellow

Ⓑ blue   Ⓓ orange

❸ **Analyze:** What is the most common worry for kids 8 to 11 years old?

 Summarize

1. ▶ **WRITE** What is the topic of "The Bully's Victim"?

_____

_____

2. **UNDERLINE** Find two details in "The Bully's Victim" that tell about the topic.

3. Summarize the section in your own words to a partner.

CRITICAL READING

Synthesize

▶ **WRITE** If you saw two of your friends bullying someone, what would you do?

_____

_____

_____

✓ Skills Check

1. ▶ **WRITE** What is the topic of "Fighting Back"?

_____

_____

2. **UNDERLINE** Find three important details in "Fighting Back" that relate to the topic.

3. Summarize the section to a partner in your own words.

Word Challenge

START

1
Check two. Which two activities would be the biggest **struggle** for you?

- ☐ making a three-point shot in basketball
- ☐ writing a scary story
- ☐ spelling a big word
- ☐ cooking a family dinner

2 Context Clues

Sometimes, you'll see a word you don't know in a sentence. One way to figure out what it means is to look at the words around it. The words around it are the "context" for the word. They can give you "context clues."

What does _extraordinary_ mean? Study the context and make a guess.

- ☐ common, boring
- ☐ ugly, weird
- ☐ special, unusual
- ☐ funny

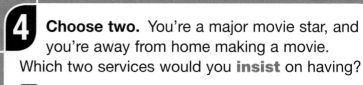

I won a gold medal for my **extraordinary** physical talent.

3
Tell a story. Complete the sentences using **injured**, **incident**, and **insisted**.

A few days ago, there was a scary _____ on the soccer field. My best friend _____ his leg pretty badly. We _____ that he go to a doctor.

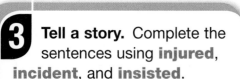

4
Choose two. You're a major movie star, and you're away from home making a movie. Which two services would you **insist** on having?

- ☐ your own limo and driver
- ☐ your favorite video games in your hotel room
- ☐ your favorite snacks on the movie set
- ☐ a personal trainer to work out with you

5
Evaluate. What is your favorite **physical** activity?

_____

What is your least favorite **physical** activity?

_____

What new **physical** activity would you like to try?

_____

6. Rank them.

Rank them. Which situation would make you the most **nervous**?

Put them in order.

1 = least **nervous**

4 = most **nervous**

_____ taking a big math test

_____ shooting a free throw in a championship basketball game

_____ jumping off the high diving board

_____ babysitting a younger sibling

7. Think about it.

Think about it. How do the people in your life put **pressure** on you? Write about it.

My family **pressures** me to

_____

My friends **pressure** me to

_____

My teachers **pressure** me to

_____

I **pressure** myself to

_____

8. Check them.

Check them. Which problems would you need an **expert**'s help with?

☐ your bike gets a flat tire

☐ your dog gets a bad cut on its paw

☐ you have to find a gift for your mom

☐ your email is not working

9. Compound Words

A compound word is made up of two smaller words. For example: *home* + *work* = *homework*.

Match a word from the first column with a word from the second column to make a compound word.

base+ball = baseball

Word 1 + Word 2 = Compound Word

foot	star	1. _____
touch	ball	2. _____
super	down	3. _____

Now use the compound words to complete the sentence.

During the _____ game, I made a

_____ and became a _____.

10. Finish them.

Finish them. Complete the sentences using the words **united**, **insists**, and **convince**.

My best friend and I are _____

in our view that baseball is the best sport. But

I can't _____ her that hockey is

a cool sport, too. She _____

that hockey is boring.

FINISH

Writing Text Type
Opinion Essay

An **opinion essay** states an opinion about an issue or topic. The writer supports the opinion with reasons, examples, and facts.

Introduction

An **introductory statement** introduces an issue the writer wants to persuade readers about.

1. UNDERLINE the **introductory statement.**

The introductory paragraph also includes a clear **focus statement** that gives the writer's opinion.

2. BOX the **focus statement.**

Body

Each body paragraph starts with a **topic sentence** about the issue.

3. UNDERLINE the **topic sentence**.

Reasons, examples, and facts support the topic sentence.

4. ✔ CHECK three supporting **reasons, examples, or facts**.

Language Use

Linking words and phrases introduce or connect ideas.

5. CIRCLE five **linking words and phrases** in the essay.

Conclusion

The **conclusion** restates the opinion and offers a recommendation for readers.

6. ★ STAR the **conclusion**.

Student Model

Why Bullies Need Help
by Katy Chin

Bullying is a serious issue for students of all ages. Of course, most people feel sorry for victims of bullying. In my opinion, we should try to understand and help the bullies, too.

Bullies act mean because they feel bad and because they lack social skills. Many bullies have been treated badly by others. They bully because that is how they have been treated. Some kids bully to try to impress others and act cool. In fact, bullying is not cool, so the bully just ends up feeling unpopular. Bullies need better social skills. For example, they need to learn to control anger, and how to make friends.

In conclusion, bullies need help, not just punishment. Punishments may be needed, but do not teach bullies the social skills they need. Kindness, respect, and help from others may help bullies to stop bullying for good.

B   I   U

P 1

Analyze the Text Type

▶ **Work with a partner to understand the purpose and form of an opinion essay.**

Purpose: Opinion Essay

The purpose of an opinion essay is _____

Introduction

The **introductory paragraph** of an opinion essay serves two purposes. It:

1. includes an _____ that introduces the issue.

2. includes a focus statement that presents the _____

Student Model | In her introduction, Katy:

1. introduces the issue she will discuss, which is: _____

2. presents her opinion, which is: _____

Body

The **body** paragraph provides convincing reasons and evidence.

1. Each body paragraph starts with a _____

2. The rest of the body paragraph gives _____

that support the _____

Student Model

1. The topic sentence of the body paragraph is _____

_____

2. List two reasons, facts, or examples that Katy includes in her paragraph.

   • _____

   • _____

Conclusion

The **conclusion** _____ the _____ of the essay

and offers a _____

Student Model | Katy recommends that _____

_____

_____

Brainstorm

▶ Read the writing prompt. Then brainstorm reasons, examples, and facts to support each opinion.

Writing Prompt:
Do schools do enough to stop bullies? Defend your opinion.

Yes! Schools do a good job of stopping bullies.

No! Schools need to do more to stop bullying.

State Your Topic

▶ Use ideas from the idea web to help you craft your opinion.

My opinion is that _____

because _____

_____

Organize Ideas for Writing

▶ **Complete this outline with notes for your opinion essay.**

I. Introduction Introduce your opinion about the issue.

    A. Issue: _____

    B. My Claim: _____

    C. Introductory Statement: _____

    D. Focus Statement: _____

    _____

II. Body Write a topic sentence for the body paragraph that supports your claim. Then list important details that support your topic sentence.

    A. Topic Sentence _____

    _____

        Detail 1: _____

        _____

        Detail 2: _____

        _____

        Detail 3: _____

        _____

III. Conclusion In one or two sentences, restate the focus statement and offer a recommendation to readers.

    _____

    _____

    _____

    _____

    _____

    _____

    _____

Write Your Draft

▶ **Write a draft of your opinion essay.**

Writing Prompt:
Do schools do enough to stop bullying?
Defend your opinion.

WORD CHOICES	
Everyday	**Precise**
choose	select
work with	cooperate
ask	plead

_____
(title)

Introduction

▶ **Write your introductory statement.**

_____

_____

▶ **Write your focus statement.**

_____

_____

_____

▶ **Type your introductory paragraph on the computer or write it on paper. Then use these linking words and phrases to help you complete a draft of your opinion essay.**

Body

First of all, . . .	However, . . .
One reason is . . .	In fact, . . .
In addition, . . .	Finally, . . .

Conclusion

In conclusion, . . .	It is important that . . .
Therefore, . . .	Try doing . . .

Revise Your Opinion Essay

▶ **Evaluate:** Rate your essay. Then have a writing partner rate it.

Scoring Guide			
needs improvement	average	good	excellent
1	2	3	4

1. **UNDERLINE** the introductory statement. Does it introduce the issue?

   Self   1   2   3   4
   Partner   1   2   3   4

2. **BOX** the focus statement. Does it present a claim?

   Self   1   2   3   4
   Partner   1   2   3   4

3. **UNDERLINE** the topic sentence of the body paragraph.

   Self   1   2   3   4
   Partner   1   2   3   4

4. ✔**CHECK** reasons, examples, and facts. Do they support the topic sentence?

   Self   1   2   3   4
   Partner   1   2   3   4

5. **CIRCLE** linking words and phrases. Do they introduce or connect ideas?

   Self   1   2   3   4
   Partner   1   2   3   4

6. ★**STAR** the sentence that offers a recommendation for readers.

   Self   1   2   3   4
   Partner   1   2   3   4

▶ **Discuss:** Give feedback on your partner's opinion essay.

1. Start with a positive comment about your partner's opinion essay.

   You did a good job of _____

   _____

   I like the way you _____

   _____

2. Give your partner suggestions for revision.

   I have a question about _____

   _____

   This idea would be clearer if you _____

   _____

   _____

3. Answer any questions your partner has about your suggestions.

4. Ask your partner for feedback. Use the frames below to summarize your partner's feedback.

   I did a good job of . . .
   The strongest parts of my essay are . . .
   You had a question about . . .
   Two changes I need to make are . . .

▶ **Revise:** Now, revise your opinion essay.

Grammar USING CORRECT VERB TENSE

The **tense** of a verb shows when the action happens.

- A **present-tense verb** shows action that is happening now.
- A **past-tense verb** shows action in the past. Most end in *-ed*.

Examples

Present-Tense Verb	Past-Tense Verb
Bullies **pick** on some kids at recess.	Bullies **picked** on my brother yesterday.
A bully **teases** my friend.	The bully **teased** her all last year.

▶ **Identify the tense of the verb in each sentence below by writing *present* or *past* on the line to the right.**

1. Girls in Keesha's class called her names. *past*

2. Some girls tease younger students. _____

3. A popular girl at school bullied Karen. _____

4. Karen complained to her family and teachers. _____

5. The principal helps protect students. _____

Some verbs have irregular past-tense forms. These verbs don't end in *-ed*.

Example

Present-Tense Verb	Past-Tense Verb
I am happy when I **see** my friends.	I am happy that I **saw** my friends.
I often **think** about my friend who moved away.	Yesterday, I **thought** about my friend who moved away.

▶ **Rewrite the sentences below using the past tense of the verb.**

6. Some kids at school want attention.

_____

7. Karen and Kelsey talk about the bullies.

_____

8. The teachers punish the bullies at my school.

_____

9. Those mean girls pick on the new student.

_____

▶ **Edit Your Draft.** Take a close look at each sentence in your draft. **Do they use correct verb tenses?** Fix any that do not.

Mechanics USING COMMAS IN A SERIES

Items in a series are separated by **commas**.

- A series is a list of the same kinds of words.
- Commas follow every item in the series except the last one.

Examples

Correct	Incorrect
Kids, parents, and teachers all want bullying to end.	Kids parents and teachers all want bullying to end.

▶ **Find and correct five errors in this paragraph.**

Student Model

> Bullying is a problem in many schools. However, most schools do a good job of stopping bullies. In my school, we hardly ever have problems with bullying. There is little fisical bullying verbal bullying or relationship bullying. Our school has a no-bullying policy, so bullys are always punished. Also, every classroom has a list of rules about bullying. It described what bullying victims can do to fight back.

CHECK AND CORRECT

- ❑ **UNDERLINE** two comma errors and correct them.
- ❑ Correct one verb tense error.
- ❑ (CIRCLE) two spelling errors and correct them.

▶ **Edit Your Draft.** Take a close look at each sentence in your draft. **Do they use commas correctly?** Fix any that do not.

Final Draft/Present

▶ **Write a final draft of your essay on the computer or on paper. Check it again and correct any errors before you present it.**

Focus Skill | Use the Internet

Evaluate a Website Registration Page

This website invites you to write a book review. You can also read reviews by other students. Before using the website, reviewers need to fill out a registration form.

▶ **Read this registration page, then answer the questions.**

MARK IT

• **UNDERLINE** the name of this website.

• **CIRCLE** the link you can click to read the website's privacy policy.

• ★**STAR** two places where you should type a password.

THUMBS-UP READS!
An e-Club for Young Readers

Certified safe for all ages!

REGISTER | **ABOUT THIS BLOG** | **MEET OUR REVIEWERS** | **PRIVACY POLICY**

Name*

Username (not your real name)*

Password*

Confirm Password*

Password Safety Word/Phrase*

Parent's or Guardian's Email*

Gender* Male

Birthday* MM-DD-YYYY

(Fields marked with a star (*) are required)

☐ I accept the "Thumbs-Up Reads!" rules.

SUBMIT

---

❶ What does this symbol (*) mean?

Ⓐ This is important.

Ⓑ This is required.

Ⓒ This is optional.

Ⓓ Click here for more information.

❷ What should you click to enter your information after completing the form?

Ⓐ Gender

Ⓑ "Thumbs-Up Reads!" rules

Ⓒ Privacy Policy

Ⓓ Submit

❸ Some passwords are more secure than others. Which kinds of passwords are safest? Make a choice, and explain.

☐ passwords with only letters

☐ passwords with only numbers

☐ passwords with letters and numbers

_____

_____

_____

_____

_____

School Counselor
Vanessa Gomez

Meet a counselor who helps students get along with each other.

▶ **Read the interview and job information. Then answer the questions about Vanessa Gomez's job.**

S **Scholastic: As a counselor, do you deal with Internet bullying?**

Vanessa Gomez: If a student is posting mean things online about another student, we talk with both kids. If the bullying doesn't stop, we bring in the vice principal or principal and they can punish students. Usually, we also bring in the parents.

S **How do you deal with bullying inside the school?**

We teach students how to notice warning signs of bullying. We have "concerned person forms" in every classroom. If students are worried about bullying, they can fill out a form about it.

S **What do you do with the forms?**

We read the forms, then we bring students in to talk to us. We ask them what is bothering them. It's not about punishing kids, it's about helping them deal with problems they are having with anger or how to cope with problems in their home life.

ON THE JOB

LOCATION
Moreno Valley, California

EDUCATION
Master's degree
in Counseling

RESPONSIBILITIES
• Works to prevent violence
• Helps students succeed
• Teaches online etiquette

SKILLS
• Communicating
• Solving problems
• Understanding others

SALARY
$32,000–$48,000

FAVORITE PART OF THE JOB
"It's not just my job, it's my passion. My job is to help kids overcome barriers to learning."

CAREER CONNECTION

Education & Training
www.careerclusters.org

Related Jobs
• teacher
• psychologist
• teacher's aide

❶ **Vanessa deals with helping kids keep safe on the Internet. What happens if students do not stop bullying online?**

_____

_____

❷ **Do you think Vanessa's job makes a difference? Mark the line.**

```
●———————●———————●———————●———————●
1         2         3         4         5
```
makes a difference   does not make a difference

❸ **Vanessa's job does / does not (circle one) make a difference because** _____

_____

Focus Skills Evaluate Risk | Ask Questions

How can you stop a bully?

Bullying is a problem in many schools. Create a page for your school's website called **"Top Three Ways to Stop Bullying."**

❶ **Identify issues.** How can bullying affect a student's life? List examples from the Workshop readings and your own ideas.

- ______________________________
- ______________________________
- ______________________________

❷ **Collaborate.** List three problems that students may be having with bullying in your school.

- ______________________________
- ______________________________
- ______________________________

❸ **Evaluate risk.** What can you do if you are bullied at school? List five ideas for responding to bullies. Then list possible risks that you could face with each response.

Response to Bullies	Risks

❹ **Rate your ideas.** Cross out any responses that are too risky. Then circle your top three responses to bullying. Rate them 1 (best idea) to 3.

⑤ **Use your best ideas to create your Web page.**

www.longlots.org

About Our School | Visitor Information | School Calendar

Top Three Ways to Stop Bullying

Students at our school need to know how to deal with bullying. Bullying can lead to problems such as _____

_____

_____

Here are three effective ways to respond to bullies.

1. _____

_____

_____

_____

2. _____

_____

_____

_____

3. _____

_____

_____

_____

This page was last updated on _____

Comprehension

▶ **Fill in the circle next to the correct answer.**

CRITICAL READING

1. Analyze: The writers of the "Stop All Bullies!" letter want _____.

Ⓐ to get a bully kicked out of school

Ⓑ the principal to stop bullying students

Ⓒ to start an anti-bullying group at school

Ⓓ all fifth-grade bullies to be punished

> **Here's a Tip.**
> Always fill in bubbles completely when you are taking multiple-choice tests. If you don't, the computer might not be able to read your answer.

2. If you are bullied by a girl, why might it be hard to get help?

Ⓐ 911 does not respond to calls from students.

Ⓑ Many girl bullies tease, which is not as obvious as physical fighting.

Ⓒ Many people think girls have the right to bully anyone they want.

Ⓓ The fights are so loud that no one can hear the victim's request for help.

CRITICAL READING

3. Synthesize: Which statement best summarizes the article "Girl Fight"?

Ⓐ Most girls end up in a fight sooner or later.

Ⓑ Girls do not usually throw punches so their fights are not very serious.

Ⓒ Girls usually fight with words, but it's just as serious as using punches.

Ⓓ Girls are very good at dealing with the problem of bullying.

4. Bullies tend to pick on kids who seem _____.

Ⓐ hard to upset

Ⓑ easy to upset

Ⓒ hard to talk to

Ⓓ popular

5. About how many kids ages 8–11 are worried about bullies?

Ⓐ more than half

Ⓑ almost all

Ⓒ only a few

Ⓓ none

Vocabulary

▶ **Fill in the circle next to the correct definition for each underlined word.**

1. Winning the championship game would be a <u>struggle</u> unless we were <u>united</u>.

   Ⓐ a surprise; saddened   Ⓒ a great experience; injured
   Ⓑ something easy to do;   Ⓓ something hard to do;
      cheated by someone   came together

2. <u>Experts</u> agree that dealing with bullies can be difficult.

   Ⓐ gym teachers   Ⓒ a bully's victims
   Ⓑ people with no experience Ⓓ people with special knowledge

3. Dina <u>convinced</u> the principal that kids were under <u>pressure</u> from bullies.

   Ⓐ fooled; friendship   Ⓒ apologized to; agreement
   Ⓑ requested; training in a   Ⓓ made someone believe;
      special skill   strong influence

▶ **Use context clues to choose the definition of the underlined word.**

4. My cousin is so <u>obstinate</u>, you can't convince her to do anything!

   Ⓐ easy to please   Ⓒ stubborn
   Ⓑ funny-looking   Ⓓ happy

▶ **Which word in this sentence is a compound word?**

5. The principal explained the school guidelines to the new students.

   Ⓐ principal   Ⓒ students
   Ⓑ school   Ⓓ guidelines

Short Answer

CRITICAL READING

▶ **Synthesize: Use what you've read in this Workshop to answer the question. Check your spelling and grammar.**

What could you do to stop bullying in your school? Describe one or more actions you could take, and explain how it would help stop bullying.

_____

_____

_____

WORKSHOP 5

INFORMATIONAL TEXT

COMPREHENSION FOCUS
Problem and Solution

CRITICAL READING FOCUS
Analyze

Evaluate

Reading 1 King Tut's Tomb | **Encyclopedia Article**

Reading 2 The Gory Art of Mummy Making | **Magazine Article**

Reading 3 Ancient Egypt: Unlocking the Past | **Social Studies Text**

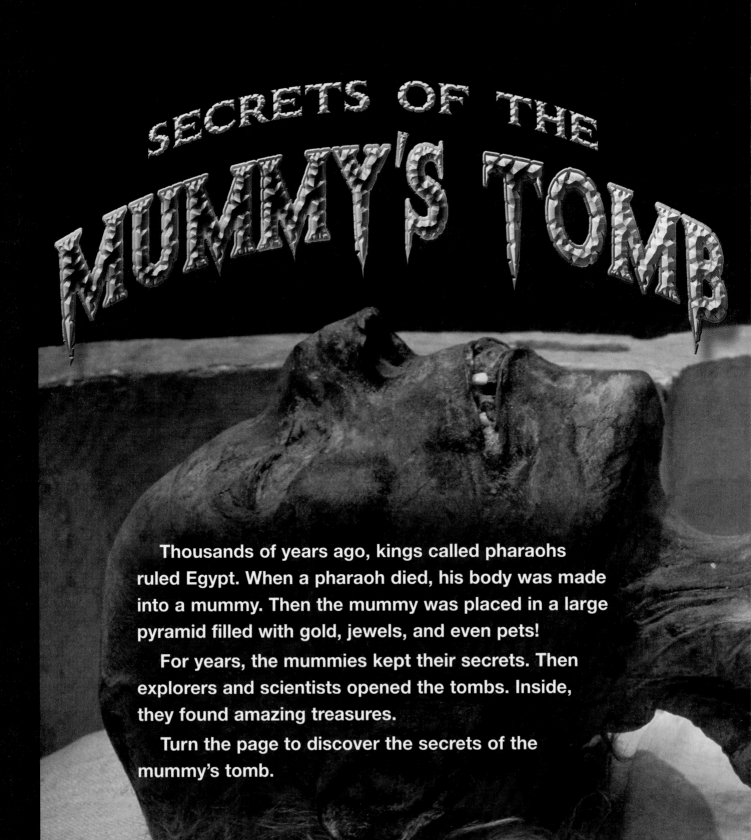

SECRETS OF THE MUMMY'S TOMB

Thousands of years ago, kings called pharaohs ruled Egypt. When a pharaoh died, his body was made into a mummy. Then the mummy was placed in a large pyramid filled with gold, jewels, and even pets!

For years, the mummies kept their secrets. Then explorers and scientists opened the tombs. Inside, they found amazing treasures.

Turn the page to discover the secrets of the mummy's tomb.

Academic Vocabulary

Target Word ▸ Read the Target Words. Rate each one using the scale below.*	Meaning ▸ Read the Target Word meanings. Write in the missing words.	Examples ▸ Finish the Target Word examples below. Write in the missing ones.
examine (p. 120) ex•am•ine (verb) ① ② ③ ④	to look at or study something carefully	• To solve a crime, detectives might **examine** _____ _____ • The _____ will **examine** _____ to find out why he's ill.
preserve (p. 122) pre•serve (verb) ① ② ③ ④	to _____ something from being destroyed	• I want to **preserve** my _____ _____ • _____ _____
construct (p. 124) con•struct (verb) ① ② ③ ④	to _____ something	Egyptians **constructed** pyramids thousands of years ago.
symbol (p. 124) sym•bol (noun) ① ② ③ ④	a sign or _____ that represents _____	• One **symbol** of America is the _____ • A common **symbol** for peace is _____
material (p. 127) ma•te•ri•al (noun) ① ② ③ ④	things such as wood, plastic, or cloth used to make other things	• **Materials** used to build a house include _____ • _____ _____

*Rating Scale
① = I don't know the word.   ③ = I think I know the word.
② = I've seen it or heard it.   ④ = I know it and use it.

King Tut's Tomb

The Key Idea

▶ **WRITE** What is this article mostly about?

_____

_____

VOCABULARY
 Target Word

investigate

in•ves•ti•gate (verb)

Rate It: ① ② ③ ④

Meaning

to _____

something

Example

I will **investigate** a topic for

the research project by _____

_____

_____

React and Write

▶ **WRITE** Do you think it would be fun to search for mummies? Or would it be boring and hard?

Summarize

In one or two sentences, describe what Howard Carter did. Include the topic and important details.

King Tut ruled Egypt for only a few years. But his tomb was one of the greatest discoveries of all time.

A scientist and explorer named Howard Carter found the tomb. He began searching for it in 1914. He looked in a part of Egypt called the Valley of the Kings. By 1922, Carter had a big problem. He was out of money. His team wanted to give up the search.

But Carter wasn't ready to quit. He was convinced that he should **investigate** a little longer. Later that year, a worker on Carter's team found an old stairway. It was buried under a pile of stones. When the stones were cleared away, he saw something exciting. The stairway led to a door. It was the door to King Tut's tomb!

Carter's long years of searching were worth it. Many ancient tombs had been robbed of their treasures. But Tut's tomb

The mummy case of King Tut.

was barely touched. Its many rooms were packed with gold and jewels!

Only one problem remained. Where was Tut's mummy? Carter examined every room. Finally, he located it deep inside the tomb. Today Tut is the most famous mummy in the world! _END_

| Words to Know! | **tomb** | a burial chamber |

Comprehension Focus

Problem and Solution

A **problem** is a situation or event that causes trouble. A **solution** is what fixes the problem. To find a problem and its solution:

- Look for the problem.
- Find the solution to the problem.

▶ **Complete this chart with two problems and solutions from "King Tut's Tomb."**

Problem

_____

_____

_____

_____

_____

Solution

_____

_____

_____

_____

_____

Problem

_____

_____

_____

_____

_____

Solution

_____

_____

_____

_____

_____

The Key Idea

▶ **WRITE** What is this article mostly about?

_____

_____

VOCABULARY
Target Word

task

task (noun)

Rate It: ① ② ③ ④

Meaning

a job, or _____ to be done

Example

Some household **tasks** include

_____

_____

React and Write

▶ **WRITE** Would you touch a mummy if you could? Why or why not?

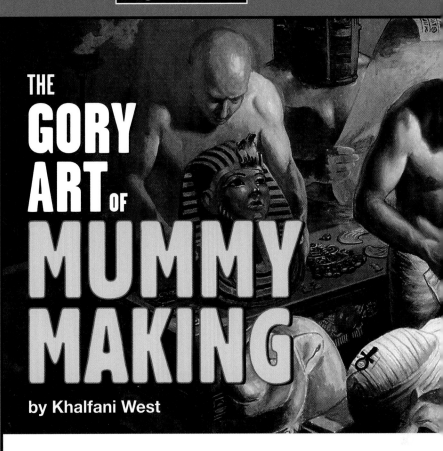

THE GORY ART OF MUMMY MAKING

by Khalfani West

Here's how to preserve a dead body before it rots!

Death was a whole new life for the ancient Egyptians. They believed that the dead went to live in another world. But there was one big problem. The dead needed their bodies to live in that world. And dead bodies rot fast. So the Egyptians found a way to solve the problem. They preserved dead bodies by making them into mummies.

Taking the Insides Out

When a body dies, its organs rot first. The organs are parts like the brain, eyes, liver, and lungs. The mummy makers' first **task** was to take out those parts. They used a special hook to remove the brain. The hook went up the body's nose. With each pull, a piece of brain popped out!

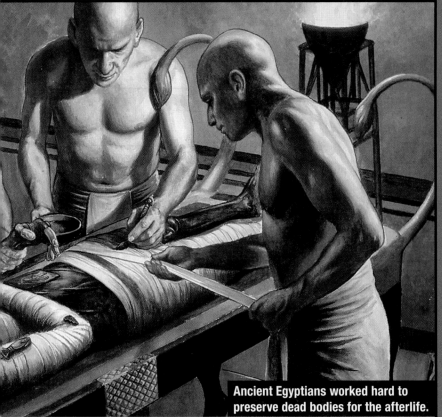

Ancient Egyptians worked hard to preserve dead bodies for the afterlife.

Dry as Bone

Next, the Egyptians dealt with another problem. Dead bodies are full of water. Water makes things rot. So, the mummy makers covered each body with salt. The salt absorbed water like a sponge. After 40 days, the body was dry as bone.

Next, it was time to make the body look nice. First, the Egyptians coated it with tree sap. The sap dried and became a hard shell. Then the mummy makers stuffed the body with rags. The rags helped it keep its shape. They even put false eyes into the face. Finally, the mummy was ready for wrapping. ➤

Words to Know!   **absorb**   to soak up liquid

📖 Problem and Solution

1. ▶ **WRITE** What problem did the mummy makers face?

_____

_____

_____

_____

2. <u>UNDERLINE</u> Identify two ways that the mummy makers tried to solve this problem.

CRITICAL READING
🧠 Analyze

▶ **WRITE** Based on the description in the text, which would be the hardest step in the mummy-making process? Explain.

_____

_____

_____

_____

_____

_____

Active Reading

★**STAR** What might be included with a mummy in its case?

VOCABULARY
Target Word

system

sys•tem (noun)

Rate It: ① ② ③ ④

Meaning

a way of _____

Example

My **system** for cleaning my

room is to _____

_____

React and Write

▶ **WRITE** Would you want to see someone make a mummy in real life? Would that be cool—or gross?

Summarize

In one or two sentences, summarize the topic and important details in "All Wrapped Up."

This cat was an Egyptian's pet. Now its mummy is on display at a museum.

All Wrapped Up

Once a body was dry, the Egyptians had one more problem. They needed to protect the body. So they wrapped the body in layers of cloth. First, they cut the cloth into long strips. Then they wound the strips around the head and body. Between the layers, they put jewels and good luck charms. Finally, they put a mask on the mummy. The mask looked like the dead person's real face.

Next, mummy makers constructed a special box. The box was called a mummy case. The dead person's favorite things were packed in the case. Symbols of the person's wealth were also put inside. Even dead pets were put near the mummy case! The pets were mummies, too, of course.

The Test of Time

How did the Egyptians' **system** work out? Some mummies are now more than 5,000 years old! And they still look great. Examine them yourself. You can find them in museums around the world. ⟨END⟩

Words to Know! | **layer** something that is placed on or exists between other things

Comprehension Focus
Problem and Solution

▶ Complete this chart with problems and solutions from "The Gory Art of Mummy Making."

Problem

Solution

Problem

Solution

The Key Idea

▶ **WRITE** What is this article mostly about?

_____

_____

VOCABULARY

Target Word

transport

trans•port (verb)

Rate It: ① ② ③ ④

Meaning

to _____ an object

or person

Example

One way to **transport** bricks

is by _____

React and Write

▶ **WRITE** How would workers build a pyramid today? What tools might they use?

Unlocking the Past

by Sana Levine

In Egypt, pyramids were the tombs of kings. Find out how pyramids were built!

Great Kings, Great Pyramids

The pyramids of Egypt are more than 4,000 years old. They were built for the pharaohs, who were kings of Egypt. When a pharaoh died, his body was made into a mummy. Then the mummy was buried inside a pyramid.

Building a pyramid was a huge project. The average pyramid took twenty years to build! It also took lots of planning and supplies. To solve that problem, a pharaoh started planning his burial pyramid once he came to power.

Getting Ready to Build

Preparing the pyramid site was hard work. The pyramid base had to be flat. Otherwise, the pyramid would be lopsided! So builders came up with different methods for making the base flat. Sometimes, they dug trenches in the ground. Then they flooded the trenches. Bumps of sand appeared above the water. The sand was leveled off and made flat.

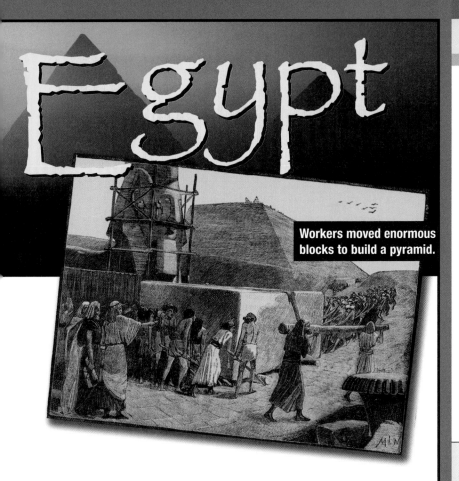

Workers moved enormous blocks to build a pyramid.

Builders also had to deal with another problem. The sides of the pyramid had to be exactly the same distance apart. If not, they wouldn't meet at the top! So, four priests marked where each side should go. First, they stood at the center of the site. Then, one priest walked north. Another walked east. The third went south. The fourth went west. They all walked the exact same distance from the center.

Getting materials to the site was a problem, too. Pyramids are made of huge, heavy stone blocks that are very hard to **transport**. So, workers carved the blocks out of quarries next to the Nile River. In the summer, the river flooded. The water rose high. Then, workers could float the blocks across the river to the pyramid site. ➤

| Words to Know! | **trenches** long, narrow ditches |

Problem and Solution

1. UNDERLINE Mark the sentences that tell how the problem of making a flat base was solved.

2. ▷ WRITE What problem would there be if the sides weren't the same distance apart?

_____

_____

_____

3. CIRCLE How did workers get the heavy blocks to the site of the pyramid?

REVIEW
Summarize

What is the topic of "Getting Ready to Build"? What are two important details? Summarize the section to a partner.

CRITICAL READING
Evaluate

▷ **WRITE** On a scale of 1–10, how creative were the methods used to build the pyramids? Explain your rating.

_____

_____

_____

_____

_____

Active Reading

★**STAR** What was placed at the top of a pyramid?

VOCABULARY
Target Word

value

val•ue (noun)

Rate It: ① ② ③ ④

Meaning

what something is _____

Example

_____

_____

are objects of great **value**.

React and Write

▶ **WRITE** Would you be afraid to go into a pyramid? Why or why not?

Summarize

▶ **WRITE** Summarize the topic and important details in the social studies text "Ancient Egypt: Unlocking the Past."

Pushing Half-Ton Blocks

Once on land, the heavy blocks were hauled to the pyramid site. But this presented another problem. Moving heavy blocks was much harder on land than on water.

Workers found solutions. When the ground was smooth, they could put wooden rollers under the blocks. Then they rolled the blocks to the site. But when the ground was rough, workers had to pull the blocks with ropes. One man shouted directions. The others yelled together. As they yelled, they pulled. That way, they were sure to pull at the same time.

Finally, the blocks were put in place, layer by layer. Each layer became a platform. The next layer was built on top. Workers constructed ramps made of mud to pull up each layer of blocks. At the very top, workers usually placed a miniature pyramid.

TEXT FEATURE Reading a Diagram

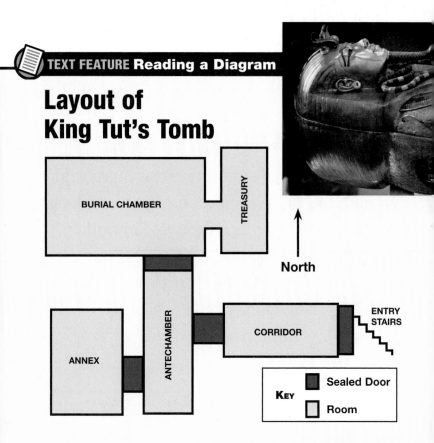

Layout of King Tut's Tomb

BURIAL CHAMBER

TREASURY

North

ANNEX

ANTECHAMBER

CORRIDOR

ENTRY STAIRS

KEY
- Sealed Door
- Room

Keeping Out Robbers

Before the pyramid was finished, a tomb was built deep inside it. The pharaoh's mummy was placed inside the tomb. The mummy was buried with many things of **value**, like money, jewels, and furniture. There was even a jar with the pharaoh's liver in it!

From the tomb, a passage led outside. It was the only way out. It was also a way in for tomb robbers. The pyramid builders tried to solve this problem. They made the door to the passage look like solid stone. Some also built traps! In the dark, a robber might step on a fake stone. Then he'd fall into a deep hole. Sadly, these solutions didn't always work. Many tombs were robbed.

However, the great pyramids have lasted for many centuries. They are a symbol of ancient Egyptian culture. If you ever go to Egypt, you can still see them rising up from the sand. _END_

Words to Know!	**centuries** periods of one hundred years

A diagram provides information with drawings and labels.

❶ How many rooms are in King Tut's tomb?

   Ⓐ two   Ⓑ three   Ⓒ five   Ⓓ six

❷ What do the dark blue sections represent?

   Ⓐ sealed doors   Ⓒ guards

   Ⓑ treasures   Ⓓ traps for robbers

❸ **Analyze:** The doors between the entryway and King Tut's mummy were all sealed. Why?

_____

_____

 Problem and Solution

1. ▷ **WRITE** How did workers push the heavy blocks across land? Identify two solutions.

• _____

_____

• _____

_____

2. <u>UNDERLINE</u> How did workers move the blocks up the pyramid?

CRITICAL READING
Evaluate

▷ **WRITE** Which solution for moving heavy blocks do you think was the most impressive? Why?

_____

_____

_____

_____

✓ **Skills Check**

1. ▷ **WRITE** What problem did the builders face after they put the pharaoh and his belongings in the pyramid?

_____

2. <u>UNDERLINE</u> Mark two ways they tried to solve this problem.

Word Challenge

I'm **wrapping** a present for my mom.

START

1 Make a guess.
How long would it take you to **construct** each item?

	Minutes
a snow fort	_____
a sand castle	_____
a hand puppet	_____

2 Homophones

Homophones are words that sound alike but have different spellings and meanings. Examples are *piece* and *peace*, and *wrap* and *rap*.

► **Match each word to its homophone.**

two	hear	week

Homophone

here	_____
too	_____
weak	_____

► **Fill in each sentence with a homophone.**

- It's been a _____ since I saw my friend Ricky!
- You're going swimming? I want to go, _____!
- Please turn up the music, so I can _____ it better.

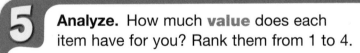

I'm **rapping** about wrapping a present for my mom!

3 Identify them. Which two of these are **tasks**?

doing dishes	_____
watching TV	_____
talking to your friends	_____
cleaning your room	_____

4 Check it. Your pet snake is sick. What's the safest way to **transport** a snake to the vet?

- ☐ hang it around your neck
- ☐ put it all by itself in a plastic bag
- ☐ throw it inside your backpack
- ☐ place it in a box with breathing holes

5 Analyze. How much **value** does each item have for you? Rank them from 1 to 4.

1 = most **value**   4 = least **value**

- ____ a bag of money
- ____ a book of family pictures
- ____ a special gift from your best friend
- ____ a shopping spree at the mall

6 **Think about it.**
Examine the photo. What kind of food do you think it is?

_____

_____

Would you eat it? Why or why not?

_____

_____

I grew this plant all by myself. I've got a **green thumb.**

7 # Idioms

An idiom is a phrase that means something different from the separate meanings of the words in the phrase. Something interesting can be called "food for thought." Something easy to do is "a piece of cake."

▶ **Match each idiom to its meaning:**

"I'm sick as a dog!"   You've got a big problem.

"You're in hot water!"   I am very sick.

▶ **Now finish these sentences:**

I was in hot water after I _____

I was sick as a dog when _____

9 **Identify it.** Write what each **symbol** stands for:

⬦ _____

☺ _____

👤 _____

Now draw another **symbol** and tell what it stands for:

_____

8 **Rate it.** What's the best way to plan a party? Rank these choices from **1** (best) to **3** (worst).

____ **Investigate** the history of celebrations. Based on what you find out, buy decorations for your party. Then, pass out invitations and celebrate!

____ First, create a **system** for organizing your party. Then, make a list of food, decorations, and people to invite.

____ First, decorate the room. Then, make a list of **materials** you'll need. Then, tell your friends to throw _you_ a party.

10 **Rank them.** What is the best way to **preserve** a leftover sandwich? Rank these methods from **1** (best) to **4** (worst).

____ wrap it in plastic   ____ put it in your pocket

____ stuff it in your desk   ____ stick it in the fridge

▶ FINISH

Writing Text Type
Informational Summary

An **informational summary** gives the key topics and ideas from a text.

▶ Read student Alan Park's summary of "The Gory Art of Mummy Making."

Student Model

Introduction

An **introductory statement** tells the text type, title, and author.

1. UNDERLINE the **introductory statement**.

A **focus statement** states the plan for the essay.

2. BOX the **focus statement**.

Body

Each body paragraph starts with a **topic sentence. Details and examples** support the topic sentence.

3. ✔CHECK five **details and examples** in the body.

Language Use

Linking words and phrases introduce and connect ideas.

4. CIRCLE six **linking words or phrases**.

Quotations from the text appear in quotation marks. The page number is given in parentheses.

5. DOUBLE UNDERLINE two **quotations** from the text.

Conclusion

The **conclusion** restates the focus statement and adds an interesting final thought.

6. ★STAR the **conclusion**.

Mummy Making in Ancient Egypt
by Alan Park

In the magazine article "The Gory Art of Mummy Making," Khalfani West explains how ancient Egyptians created mummies. Step by step, the author describes how mummy makers preserved a body successfully for thousands of years.

There were five basic steps to mummy making. First, the organs were removed from the body. Mummy makers used a hook to take out the brain. After that, the body had to be dried out, so mummy makers covered the body in salt to absorb the water. According to West, "After 40 days, the body was dry as bone" (123). Next, to preserve its appearance, the body was coated in sap and stuffed with rags. Then, it was wrapped in cloth for protection. Finally, the mummy was covered with a mask of the dead person's face.

The article ends by telling how successful ancient Egypt's mummy makers were. West states, "Some mummies are now more than 5,000 years old! And they still look great" (124).

Analyze the Text Type

▶ **Work with a partner to understand the purpose and form of an informational summary.**

Purpose: Informational Summary
An informational summary gives the key _____ from a text.

Introduction

The **introduction** of an informational summary serves two purposes. It:

1. includes an _____ that tells what text will be summarized.
2. includes a focus statement that states the _____ for the essay.

Student Model | In his introduction, Alan Park:

1. states the text type, title, and author of the piece he will summarize:

   _____

2. gives a plan for discussing the topic, which is _____

   _____

Body

The **body** of the essay gives important details about the summarized text.

1. Each body paragraph starts with a _____
2. Details and examples _____ the topic sentence.

Student Model

1. The topic sentence of Alan Park's body paragraph is _____

   _____

2. List two details Alan Park includes in his body paragraph.

   • _____

   • _____

Conclusion

The **conclusion** _____ the focus statement and adds an

interesting _____

Student Model | Park concludes _____ with an interesting

_____ from the text.

Brainstorm

▶ **Read the writing prompt. Then use the boxes to brainstorm ideas.**

Writing Prompt:
Write an informational summary of "Ancient Egypt: Unlocking the Past."

Key Idea

Details

State Your Topic

▶ **Use your ideas from the idea web to help you determine your topic.**

I plan to summarize the social studies text _____

_____,

which explains _____

_____

Organize Ideas for Writing

▶ **Complete this outline with notes for your informational summary.**

I. Introduction List details about the text you will summarize.

A. Text Type: _____

B. Title: _____

C. Author: _____

D. Topic: _____

E. My Focus Statement: _____

_____

II. Body Write a topic sentence for your body paragraph that supports the focus statement. Then list three important details or examples that support the topic sentence.

Topic Sentence _____

_____

Detail 1: _____

_____

Detail 2: _____

_____

Detail 3: _____

_____

III. Conclusion In one or two sentences, restate the focus statement and conclude your summary.

_____

_____

_____

_____

_____

_____

_____

Write Your Draft

▶ **Write a draft of your informational summary.**

Writing Prompt:
Write an informational summary of "Ancient Egypt: Unlocking the Past."

| WORD CHOICES ||
Everyday	**Precise**
move	proceed, transfer
big	enormous
find	locate

_____
(title)

Introduction

▶ **Write your introductory statement.**

In _____
(text type and title)

the author _____ discusses
(author's name)

_____
(state topic)

▶ **Write a focus statement that gives the plan for your essay.**

_____

_____

▶ **Type your introductory paragraph on the computer or write it on paper. Then use these linking words and phrases to help you complete a draft of your informational summary.**

Body

First, . . .	_Next, . . ._
To begin with, . . .	_The solution was to . . ._
Another problem was . . .	_Finally, . . ._

Conclusion

In the end, . . .	_In summary, . . ._
In conclusion, . . .	_This text explains . . ._

Revise Your Summary

▶ **Evaluate:** Rate your informational summary. Then have a writing partner rate it.

Scoring Guide			
needs improvement	average	good	excellent
1	**2**	**3**	**4**

1. <u>**UNDERLINE**</u> the introductory statement. Does it identify the text the writer will summarize?
   Self   1   2   3   4
   Partner   1   2   3   4

2. BOX the focus statement. Does it state the plan for the essay?
   Self   1   2   3   4
   Partner   1   2   3   4

3. ✔**CHECK** details and examples. Does each one support the topic sentence?
   Self   1   2   3   4
   Partner   1   2   3   4

4. CIRCLE linking words and phrases. Do they connect ideas?
   Self   1   2   3   4
   Partner   1   2   3   4

5. <u>**DOUBLE UNDERLINE**</u> two direct quotations.
   Self   1   2   3   4
   Partner   1   2   3   4

6. ★**STAR** the concluding sentence. Does it restate the focus statement?
   Self   1   2   3   4
   Partner   1   2   3   4

▶ **Discuss:** Give feedback on your partner's informational summary.

1. Start with a positive comment about your partner's summary.

You did an effective job of _____

_____

I appreciate the way you _____

_____

_____

2. Give your partner suggestions for revision.

I have a question about _____

_____

This detail would be clearer if you

_____

Answer any questions your partner has about your suggestions.

3. Ask your partner for feedback. Use the frames below to summarize your partner's feedback.

The strongest details are . . .
You appreciated the way I . . .
You had a question about . . .
An important change I can make is . . .

▶ **Revise:** Now revise your informational summary.

Grammar USING IRREGULAR VERBS

Most past-tense verbs end in *-ed*. **Irregular verbs** do not.

- You must remember the different spellings of irregular past-tense verbs.
- The verb *to be* is a common irregular verb. Its **present-tense** forms are am, is, are. Its past-tense forms are was, was, were.

Examples

Present-Tense Verb	Past-Tense Verb
Egyptians **make** the mummies.	Egyptians made the mummies.
The kings **build** pyramids.	The kings built pyramids.
The pyramids **are** made of stone.	The pyramids were made of stone.

▶ **Circle the correct past-tense verb in each sentence below.**

1. The search for King Tut [**leaded** **led**] Carter to Egypt.
2. Robbers [**stealed** **stole**] treasures from the tombs of many mummies.
3. The robbers never [**found** **finded**] the mummy of King Tut.
4. Carter [**taked** **took**] King Tut's treasures out of the tomb.
5. Workers [**made** **maked**] King Tut's tomb with many secret passages.
6. Carter was glad that he [**goed** **went**] to explore in Egypt.

▶ **Rewrite the sentences below using the past-tense form of the verb.**

7. The Egyptians **have** many rules for making mummies.

_____

_____

8. Carter **sees** the mummy in a hidden back room.

_____

_____

9. Many robbers **break** into the tombs.

_____

_____

10. Some of them **fall** into traps in the floor.

_____

_____

▶ **Edit Your Draft.** Look at each of the sentences in your draft. **Do they all use the correct form of irregular verbs?** Fix any that do not.

Mechanics USING COMMAS WITH INTRODUCTORY WORDS

A **comma** follows an opening word or phrase at the beginning of a sentence.

- *Yes*, *First*, *Next*, and *Later* are opening words.
- *In addition* and *After a while* are opening phrases.

Examples

Correct	Incorrect
Yes, King Tut was a pharaoh.	Yes King Tut was a pharaoh.
After a while, they found the tomb.	After a while they found the tomb.

▶ **Find and correct five errors in this paragraph.**

Student Model

CHECK AND CORRECT

❑ **UNDERLINE** one verb tense error and correct it.

❑ Correct two comma errors.

❑ CIRCLE two spelling errors and correct them.

Howard Carter's discovery of King Tut's tomb was one of the most amazing finds of all time. Carter searched for the tomb for eiht years. After a while his team wanted to quit, but Carter wanted to investugate a little more. Soon after that the team finded an old stairway that took them right to the door of King Tut's tomb (120)!

▶ **Edit Your Draft.** Look at the sentences in your draft. **Are all opening words and phrases followed by a comma?** Fix any that are not.

Final Draft/Present

▶ Write a final draft of your summary on the computer or on paper. Check it again and correct any errors before you present it.

Focus Skill   Analyze Media

Analyze a Website

A website can give information about a museum, business, or other organization.

▶ **Read this home page for a museum of ancient art. Then answer the questions.**

http://www.example.com/moaa

| VISIT US | EXHIBITS | CALENDAR OF EVENTS |

Welcome to MOAA, the Museum of Ancient Art

MOAA showcases creative arts from ancient cultures. Our Egypt Wing has just been expanded and redesigned. Visit and explore!

SPECIAL EVENT: Help to Wrap a Mummy!

This Saturday, January 20, visit MOAA's Egypt Wing for a special activity: mummy wrapping!

This hands-on workshop in the King Tut Room will captivate children and adults.

---

❶ **What is this museum's main purpose?**

Ⓐ offering online workshops and exhibits

Ⓑ displaying modern art from around the world

Ⓒ displaying art from ancient cultures

Ⓓ studying rulers of ancient Egypt

❷ **What special event is scheduled at the museum?**

Ⓐ a pyramid-building demonstration

Ⓑ a class about Egyptian statues

Ⓒ an interview with the museum director

Ⓓ a mummy-making workshop

❸ **What else might readers want to know about the museum and its programs?**

List two ideas for information you would add to this museum's home page. Explain each of your ideas.

A. _____

_____

_____

B. _____

_____

_____

Museum Curator
Emil Her Many Horses

Meet a curator at the National Museum of the American Indian.
He puts together multimedia exhibits with Native American themes.

▶ **Read the job log and "On the Job" column. Then answer
the questions about Emil Her Many Horses's job.**

May 2008	I have an idea for a new exhibit—the relationship between Native American tribes and horses. I present my idea to the director and other curators at the museum. They like it! The show is approved.
June 2008	We hold a fund-raising event, and raise enough money to create the exhibit. Then I spend a week searching through the museum's collection of historic items. I look for horse-related art and objects to display.
Aug. 2008	I travel to Idaho and Montana to interview tribes about their relationships with horses. I record the interviews. A photographer shoots some photos.
Sept. 2008	This month, I finalized all plans for the exhibit.
Nov. 2008	The exhibit, called "A Song for the Horse Nation," opened at the Museum of the American Indian. It will travel across the country in 2011.

① What are three types of media Emil includes in this exhibit?

_____

② How interesting do you think Emil's job is? Mark the line.

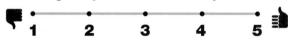

| 1 | 2 | 3 | 4 | 5 |

Not very interesting   **Very interesting**

③ I think Emil's job is/isn't (circle one) interesting because

_____

_____

ON THE JOB

LOCATION

Washington, D.C.

EDUCATION

Master's degree in Museum Studies

RESPONSIBILITIES

• Generates ideas for exhibits
• Gathers items to display
• Writes educational information

SKILLS

• Creating interesting shows to attract museum visitors
• Collaborating with coworkers
• Researching culture and history

SALARY

$33,000–$54,000

WHY IT'S REWARDING

"I am humbled by working with a team of talented people to create an exhibit that began as my idea."

CAREER CONNECTION

Education and Training
www.careerclusters.org

Related Jobs
• museum guide
• historian

Focus Skills | Use Technology for Communication | Ask Questions

Tell a mummy's tale.

In ancient Egypt, a pharaoh, or king, has died. How will his body become a mummy? What will happen to this mummy over the centuries? Plan and present a slide show to tell this mummy's story.

❶ **Ask questions.** What would your audience need to know about the ancient king's mummy? As a team, ask questions that begin with *Who*, *What*, *When*, *Where*, *Why*, and *How*. Examples: How is the mummy made? Where is it kept?

❷ **List relevant facts.** Look through the Workshop readings. Find facts that you could use in your slide show.

Reading 1: King Tut's Tomb
• _____
• _____
• _____

Reading 2: The Gory Art of Mummy Making
• _____
• _____
• _____

Reading 3: Ancient Egypt: Unlocking the Past
• _____
• _____
• _____

❸ **Brainstorm your mummy's tale.** Use your knowledge about mummies to plan four parts of your imaginary mummy's tale. Take notes here.

- After King _____ dies, _____
- Next, _____
- Then, _____
- Centuries later, _____

④ **Prepare and present your slide show.** Write one part of your mummy's tale for each numbered slide. Draw or describe an image to illustrate that part of the story.

- Before presenting your slide show, practice. Read aloud each slide, and display or describe the image that goes with it.

- **Tips:** Make sure everyone can hear and see well. Aim for a smooth delivery style.

AN EFFECTIVE SLIDE SHOW

✓ informs and entertains viewers.

✓ includes interesting facts and images.

✓ is delivered loudly and with expression.

SLIDE SHOW TITLE: _____

SLIDE 1

My slideshow.ppt

Image:

After King _____ dies, _____ _____ _____

SLIDE 2

My slideshow.ppt

Image:

Next, _____ _____ _____

SLIDE 3

My slideshow.ppt

Image:

Then, _____ _____ _____

SLIDE 4

My slideshow.ppt

Image:

Centuries later, _____ _____ _____

Comprehension

▶ **Fill in the circle next to the correct answer.**

CRITICAL READING

1. Evaluate: Why is King Tut so famous?

Ⓐ He is the current pharaoh of Egypt.

Ⓑ His tomb was one of the greatest discoveries of all time.

Ⓒ He had the largest pyramid in Egypt.

Ⓓ Many robbers died trying to open his tomb.

CRITICAL READING

2. Analyze: What problem was solved by wrapping the mummies in layers of cloth?

Ⓐ The cloth kept mummies warm.

Ⓑ The cloth helped mummies recover from broken bones.

Ⓒ The cloth fooled robbers.

Ⓓ The cloth protected the mummies after they were dried out.

Here's a Tip.
Sometimes a question asks for an answer that is not directly stated in the text. Make sure the text evidence supports your response.

3. How did mummy makers get the brain out of a dead body?

Ⓐ They cut open the skull and removed it.

Ⓑ They pulled the brain out through the nose.

Ⓒ They melted the brain and poured it from the ears.

Ⓓ They waited for the brain to rot away.

4. How did pyramid builders use the Nile River?

Ⓐ They used mud from the river for bricks.

Ⓑ They floated stone blocks across the river.

Ⓒ They coated the pyramids with river mud.

Ⓓ They used water from the river for a pond.

5. Which quality did Howard Carter possess that led to one of the greatest discoveries of all time?

Ⓐ He remained persistent.

Ⓑ He was friendly.

Ⓒ He was affectionate.

Ⓓ He showed loyalty.

Vocabulary

▶ **Fill in the circle next to the correct definition of the underlined word.**

1. Scientists <u>examine</u> mummies to discover how they were made.
   - Ⓐ to find
   - Ⓑ to make
   - Ⓒ to investigate
   - Ⓓ to preserve

2. The pyramids were <u>constructed</u> out of <u>materials</u> from nearby cliffs.
   - Ⓐ destroyed; waste
   - Ⓑ held up; glue
   - Ⓒ built; things used to create
   - Ⓓ moved; neighborhoods

3. The pyramids are <u>preserved</u> because they are a <u>symbol</u> of Egypt's history.
   - Ⓐ repaired; a stone
   - Ⓑ destroyed; a piece
   - Ⓒ forgotten; a lie
   - Ⓓ kept from being destroyed; a sign

▶ **Mark the idiom that fits best in this sentence.**

4. When I caught the flu, I was _____ for two weeks.
   - Ⓐ happy as a clam
   - Ⓑ mad as a hatter
   - Ⓒ sick as a dog
   - Ⓓ green as grass

▶ **Mark the word that fits best in this sentence.**

5. To keep it fresh, I will _____ my sandwich in plastic.
   - Ⓐ wrap
   - Ⓑ rap
   - Ⓒ hip
   - Ⓓ rip

Short Answer

CRITICAL READING

▶ **Evaluate: Use what you've read in this Workshop to answer the question below. Check your spelling and grammar.**

Why do you think people are still interested in ancient Egyptians?

_____

_____

_____

_____

WORKSHOP 6

Literary Text

COMPREHENSION FOCUS
Story Elements
CRITICAL READING FOCUS
Synthesize
Evaluate

Reading 1 The Marble Champ | **Short Story**

Reading 2 S-T-R-E-T-C-H | **Poetry**

GOOD SPORTS

Have you ever wanted to be a champ? Would you work hard enough to make it happen?

Author Gary Soto worked hard to become a famous writer. Lupe Medrano works hard, too. She's the main character in Soto's story "The Marble Champ."

Lupe wants to be the best marbles player on the playground. What will it take for her to succeed?

Academic Vocabulary

Target Word ▶ Read the Target Words. Rate each one using the scale below.*	Meaning ▶ Read the Target Word meanings. Write in the missing words.	Examples ▶ Finish the Target Word examples below. Write in the missing ones.
accurate (p. 153) *ac•cu•rate* (adjective) ① ② ③ ④	exactly _____	• _____ will help you to *be* **accurate** when _____ • _____
strengthen (p. 154) *strength•en* (verb) ① ② ③ ④	to make _____	• _____ can **strengthen** your _____ • I used tape to **strengthen** the _____
energy (p. 154) *en•er•gy* (noun) ① ② ③ ④	the strength to do things without getting tired	This meal will give me lots of **energy** to play basketball today.
encourage (p. 157) *en•cour•age* (verb) ① ② ③ ④	to praise or offer _____	• My parents **encourage** me to _____ • _____
opponent (p. 159) *op•po•nent* (noun) ① ② ③ ④	someone who is against you in a game	• My **opponent** _____ • _____ helped my **opponent** to win.

*Rating Scale
① = I don't know the word. ③ = I think I know the word.
② = I've seen it or heard it. ④ = I know it and use it.

Comprehension Focus
Story Elements

A **short story** like "The Marble Champ" is a brief work of fiction. It focuses on one or two main characters and on a single problem or conflict. To understand a short story, look for four elements:

1. Setting is where and when the story takes place. This story takes place in present-day Fresno, California.

2. Characters are the people in the story. The main character is the most important character. These are the characters in this story:

Lupe Medrano, a twelve-year-old girl   **Lupe's parents**   **Lupe's brother**

3. Plot is the sequence of events in a story. The plot contains a problem that the main character needs to solve. In "The Marble Champ," Lupe is good at a lot of things. The problem is, she's no good at sports. Can she ever become a marble champ?

4. Theme is an important message about life that the author wants readers to understand. One theme in this story is: If you work hard, you can achieve a goal.

▶ **Turn the page to begin reading Lupe's story.**

The Marble Champ

▶ **Complete this chart as you reread the story.**

	Part 1 (pp. 150–153)	**Part 2 (pp. 154–159)**	**Part 3 (pp. 160–163)**
Setting	Time: one afternoon Places: Lupe's house in Fresno, California	Time: Places:	Time: Places:
Character	Who is the main character? Describe him/her:	How does the character change?	What is the character like now?
Plot	What happens at the beginning of the story?	What happens in the middle of the story?	How does the story end?
Theme	Author's message:		

Active Reading

▶ **WRITE** What kind of runner is Lupe?

_____

_____

CRITICAL READING
Evaluate

▶ **WRITE** Lupe is good at many things. How important do you think it is for Lupe to be good at sports, too? Use a detail from the story in your response.

_____

_____

_____

_____

_____

React and Write

▶ **WRITE** What is something you are good at?

THE MARBLE CHAMP
by GARY SOTO

Lupe Medrano, a shy girl who spoke in whispers, was the school's spelling bee champion. She was also the winner of the reading contest at the public library three summers in a row, the blue ribbon awardee in the science fair, and the top student at her piano recital. Lupe was even the playground grand champion in chess. She was a straight-A student and—not counting kindergarten, when she had been stung by a wasp—never missed one day of elementary school. She had received a small trophy for this honor and had been congratulated by the mayor.

Lupe had a razor-sharp mind. But she could not make her body, no matter how much she tried, run as fast as the other girls. She begged her body to move faster, but could never beat anyone in the fifty-yard dash.

The truth was that Lupe was no good in sports. ➤

Story Elements

Setting

1. ▶ **WRITE** Look at the picture. Where might Lupe be?

_____

_____

Character

2. ✔ **CHECK** Mark four of Lupe's accomplishments.

Plot

3. ▶ **WRITE** What is Lupe's problem?

_____

_____

_____

Craft and Structure

Point of View This story is told from the **third-person point of view**. The narrator tells the story using the words _he_, _she_, _they_, and the main character's name. He or she is not a character in the story.

A third-person narrator can often tell what characters think and feel, as if reading the characters' minds.

CIRCLE Mark an example where the story's narrator tells a private wish of Lupe's.

Active Reading

★**STAR** What sport does Lupe decide to try?

VOCABULARY
Target Word

previous

pre•vi•ous (adjective)

Rate It: ① ② ③ ④

Meaning

happening _____

Example

In a **previous** Workshop

we read about _____

_____

Craft and Structure

Figurative Language describes things in fresh, lively ways. Writers use figurative language to paint a picture in readers' minds.

✔ **CHECK** Mark an example of figurative language in the first paragraph on page 153.

React and Write

▶**WRITE** What do you wish you could do well, and how could you improve at it?

She could not catch a pop-up or figure out in which direction to kick the soccer ball. One time she kicked the ball at her own goal and scored a point for the other team. She was no good at baseball or basketball either. She even had a hard time making a hula hoop stay on her hips.

It wasn't until last year, when she was eleven years old, that she learned how to ride a bike. And even then she had to use training wheels. She could walk in the swimming pool but couldn't swim. And she chanced roller skating only when her father held her hand.

"I'll never be good at sports," she fumed one rainy day. She was laying on her bed gazing at the shelf her father had made to hold her awards. "I wish I could win something, anything, even marbles."

At the word "marbles," she sat up. "That's it. Maybe I could be good at playing marbles." She hopped out of bed and rummaged through the closet. Finally, she found a can full of her brother's marbles. She poured the rich glass treasure on her bed and picked five of the most beautiful marbles.

Words to Know!	**gazing** looking at something for a long time

"I wish I could win something, anything, even marbles."

She smoothed her bedspread. Then she practiced shooting, softly at first so that her aim would be accurate. The marble rolled from her thumb and clicked against the targeted marble. But the target wouldn't budge. She tried again and again. Her aim became accurate. But the power from her thumb made the marble move only an inch or two. Then she realized that the bedspread was slowing the marbles. She also had to admit that her thumb was weaker than the neck of a newborn chick.

She looked out the window. The rain was letting up, but the ground was too muddy to play. She sat cross-legged on the bed, rolling her five marbles between her palms. Yes, she thought, I could play marbles. And marbles is a sport. At that moment she realized that she had only two weeks to practice. The playground championship, the same one her brother had entered the **previous** year, was coming up. She had a lot to do. ➤

Story Elements

Setting

1. ⬭CIRCLE⬭ Lupe practices marbles in her bedroom. Mark details that let you know this.

Character

2. ▶ WRITE What word would you use to describe Lupe's feelings about playing marbles?

_____

_____

Plot

3. ▶ WRITE How does Lupe start to solve her problem?

_____

_____

_____

_____

Theme

4. **UNDERLINE** A theme in this story is: If you work hard, you can achieve a goal. Mark a sentence about something Lupe does to reach her goal.

▶ Now go to page 149. Add details to Part 1 of the chart.

Active Reading

★**STAR** What advice does Lupe's brother give her about playing marbles?

VOCABULARY
 Target Word

exhaustion

ex•haus•tion (noun)

Rate It: ① ② ③ ④

Meaning

the state of being _____

_____

Example

Kim's **exhaustion** kept her

from _____

CRITICAL READING
 Synthesize

▶ **WRITE** Do you predict that Lupe's hard work will pay off? Use story details to explain your response.

_____

_____

_____

 React and Write

▶ **WRITE** Do you think Lupe has what it takes to be a marble champ? Why or why not?

She squeezed a rubber eraser one hundred times, hoping it would strengthen her thumb.

• •

To strengthen her wrists, she decided to do twenty push-ups on her fingertips, five at a time. "One, two, three . . ." she groaned. By the end of the first set she was breathing hard. Her muscles burned from **exhaustion**. She did one more set and decided that was enough push-ups for the first day.

She squeezed a rubber eraser one hundred times, hoping it would strengthen her thumb. This seemed to work because the next day her thumb was sore. She could hardly hold a marble in her hand, let alone send it flying with power. So Lupe rested that day and listened to her brother. He gave her tips on how to shoot: get low, aim with one eye, and place one knuckle on the ground.

"Think 'eye and thumb'—and let it rip!" he said.

After school the next day she left her homework in her backpack. She practiced three hours straight, taking time only to eat a candy bar for energy. With a popsicle stick, she drew an odd-shaped circle and tossed in four marbles. She used her shooter, a milky agate with hypnotic swirls, to blast them. Her thumb had become stronger.

After practice, she squeezed the eraser for an hour. Lupe ate dinner with her left hand to spare her shooting hand. She said nothing to her parents about her dreams of athletic glory. ➤

Story Elements

Setting

1. ▶ **WRITE** Where does the action in this part of the story take place?

_____

_____

Character

2. ▶ **WRITE** How has Lupe changed?

_____

_____

_____

_____

Plot

3. ▶ **WRITE** At this point in the story, how close is Lupe to solving her problem?

_____

_____

_____

Theme

4. **UNDERLINE** A theme in this story is: If you work hard, you can achieve a goal.

Mark three details about what Lupe does to reach her goal.

Active Reading

▶ **WRITE** Whom does Lupe beat at marbles?

_____

_____

Craft and Structure

Tone When story characters speak in short lines and use everyday language, their conversation has a casual **tone**. If characters speak in perfect English and in complete sentences, the tone is more formal.

▶ **WRITE** When Lupe and her family speak, is their tone casual or formal? Use an example to help you explain.

_____

_____

_____

_____

_____

React and Write

▶ **WRITE** Do you think Lupe is nervous about the upcoming championship? Why or why not?

Practice, practice, practice. Squeeze, squeeze, squeeze. Lupe got better and beat her brother. Then she beat Alfonso, a neighbor kid who was supposed to be a champ.

"Man, she's bad!" Alfonso said. "She can beat the other girls for sure. I think."

The weeks passed quickly. Lupe worked so hard that one day, while she was drying dishes, her mother asked why her thumb was swollen.

"It's muscle," Lupe explained. "I've been practicing for the marbles championship."

"You, honey?" Her mother knew Lupe was no good at sports.

"Yeah, I beat Alfonso. And he's pretty good."

That night, over dinner, Mrs. Medrano said, "Honey, you should see Lupe's thumb."

"Huh?" Mr. Medrano said, wiping his mouth and looking at his daughter.

"Show your father."

"Do I have to?" an embarrassed Lupe asked.

"Go on, show your father."

Reluctantly, Lupe raised her hand and flexed her thumb. You could see the muscle.

The father put down his fork. He asked, "What happened?"

"Dad, I've been working out. I've been squeezing an eraser."

"Why?"

"I'm going to enter the marbles championship."

Her father looked at her mother and then back

| Words to Know! | **reluctantly** | not wanting to do something |

at his daughter. "When is it, honey?"

"This Saturday. Can you come?"

The father had been planning to play racquetball with a friend Saturday. But he said he would be there. He knew his daughter thought she was no good at sports. He wanted to encourage her. He even rigged some lights in the backyard so she could practice after dark. He squatted with one knee on the ground, entranced by the sight of his daughter easily beating her brother.

The day of the championship began with a cold blustery sky. The sun was a silvery light behind slate clouds.

"I hope it clears up," her father said. He rubbed his hands together as he returned from getting the newspaper. They ate breakfast and paced nervously around the house waiting for 10:00 to arrive. Then they walked the two blocks to the playground (though Mr. Medrano wanted to drive so Lupe wouldn't get tired). She signed up and was assigned her first match on baseball diamond number three. ➤

| Words to Know! | **entranced** amazed, enchanted |

Story Elements

Setting

1. **CIRCLE** What is the weather like on the morning of the championship?

2. ▶ **WRITE** Where does the championship take place?

_____

_____

Character

3. **UNDERLINE** Mark a detail that shows how Lupe is becoming a better marbles player.

Plot

4. ▶ **WRITE** What key events happen in this part of the story?

_____

_____

_____

_____

Theme

5. ✔ **CHECK** Mark what Lupe's father does to help her reach her goal.

Active Reading

★**STAR** How does Lupe do in her first match?

VOCABULARY

Target Word

proceed

pro•ceed (verb)

Rate It: ① ② ③ ④

Meaning

to _____ with something

Example

After lunch, we will **proceed**

to _____

Craft and Structure

Plot Devices: Suspense An author builds suspense by keeping readers guessing about what might happen next.

▶ **WRITE** How does the author build suspense in this scene?

_____

_____

_____

React and Write

▶ **WRITE** Lupe invites the girls she beats to join her group. Would you do the same? Explain.

Lupe, walking between her brother and her father, shook from the cold, not nerves. She took off her mittens, and everyone stared at her thumb. Someone asked, "How can you play with a broken thumb?" Lupe smiled and said nothing.

> " *Just think of the marbles, not the girl. And let your thumb do the work.* "

She beat her first opponent easily. She felt sorry for the girl because she didn't have anyone to cheer for her. Except for her sack of marbles, she was all alone. Lupe invited the girl, whose name was Rachel, to stay with them. She smiled and said, "OK." The four of them walked to a card table in the middle of the outfield, where Lupe was assigned another opponent.

She also beat this girl, a fifth-grader named Yolanda. Lupe asked her to join their group. They **proceeded** to more matches and more wins. Soon there was a crowd of people following Lupe to the finals to play a girl in a baseball cap. This girl seemed dead serious. She never even looked at Lupe.

"I don't know, Dad, she looks tough."

Rachel hugged Lupe and said, "Go get her."

"You can do it," her father encouraged. "Just think of the marbles, not the girl. And let your thumb do the work."

The other girl broke first and earned one marble. She missed her next shot. Lupe, one eye closed, her thumb quivering with energy, blasted two marbles out of the circle but missed her next shot. Her opponent earned two more before missing. She stamped her foot and said "Shoot!" The score was three to two in favor of Miss Baseball Cap.

The referee stopped the game. "Back up, please, give them room," he shouted. Onlookers had gathered too tightly around the players. ➤

Words to Know! **quivering** shaking

Story Elements

Setting

1. **CIRCLE** What effect does the cold weather have on Lupe?

Character

2. **WRITE** Lupe makes friends with the girls she beats. What does that say about her?

_____

_____

Plot

3. **WRITE** How is Lupe doing in the championship?

_____

_____

_____

➤ Now go to page 149. Add details to Part 2 of the chart.

Short Story

Active Reading

★ **STAR** Who wins the final match?

VOCABULARY

Target Word

rely

re•ly (verb)

Rate It: ① ② ③ ④

Meaning

to need and _____

someone

Example

I **rely** on _____

to help me with _____

_____

CRITICAL READING

Synthesize

▶ **WRITE** What advice might Lupe give to a friend who wants to win a contest?

_____

_____

_____

React and Write

▶ **WRITE** Have you ever been in a competition? How did competing make you feel?

Lupe then earned three marbles. She was set to get her fourth when a gust of wind blew dust in her eyes. She missed badly. Her opponent quickly scored two marbles, tying the game, and moved ahead six to five on a lucky shot. Then she missed. Lupe, whose eyes felt scratchy when she blinked, **relied** on instinct and thumb muscle to score the tying point. It was now six to six, with only three

Words to Know! | **instinct** a natural feeling

marbles left. Lupe blew her nose and studied the angles. She dropped to one knee, steadied her hand, and shot so hard she cracked two marbles from the circle. She was the winner!

"I did it!" Lupe said under her breath. She rose from her knees, which hurt from bending all day, and hugged her father. He hugged her back and smiled.

Everyone clapped, except Miss Baseball Cap. She made a face and stared at the ground. Lupe told her she was a great player, and they shook hands. A newspaper photographer took pictures of the two girls standing shoulder-to-shoulder, with Lupe holding the trophy. ➤

Story Elements

Setting

1. **CIRCLE** How does the wind affect Lupe's game?

Character

2. ✔ **CHECK** Which word best describes how Lupe acts during the tournament?
   - ❏ nervous
   - ❏ confident
   - ❏ careless
   - ❏ mean

Plot

3. ▶ **WRITE** What important event happens in this part of the story?

_____

_____

Theme

4. ▶ **WRITE** A theme in this story is: If you work hard, you can achieve a goal.

   What part of Lupe's goal has she reached so far?

_____

_____

_____

_____

🔆 Active Reading

★**STAR** What does Lupe think at the end of the story?

VOCABULARY
◎ Target Word

display

dis•play (verb)

Rate It: ① ② ③ ④

Meaning

to _____ something

Example

I **display** my _____

_____

in my bedroom.

❗ React and Write

▶**WRITE** What could you do to improve a skill that is important to you?

🔲 Make Inferences

How does Lupe feel about herself now that she has won the championship? Explain.

"You did it, thumb. You made me champion. "

Meet the Author

GARY SOTO

Childhood: Soto was born in 1952 and grew up in Fresno, California. He uses his childhood as the basis for many of his books. His stories are often set in Fresno's Mexican-American community. Soto's stories focus on his characters' feelings and experiences.

Books and Poetry: *Baseball in April and Other Stories* (this book contains "The Marble Champ"), *Too Many Tamales, Crazy Weekend, Summer on Wheels. Neighborhood Odes, Fearless Fernie*

In His Words: "I discovered that reading builds a life inside the mind."

Lupe then played the winner of the boys' division. After a poor start, she beat him eleven to four. She blasted the marbles, shattering one into sparkling slivers of glass. Her opponent looked on glumly as Lupe did what she did best—win!

The head referee and the President of the Fresno Marble Association stood with Lupe as she **displayed** her trophies for the newspaper photographer. Lupe shook hands with everyone, including a dog who had come over to see what the commotion was all about.

That night, the family went out for pizza. They set the two trophies on the table for everyone in the restaurant to see. People came up to congratulate Lupe. She felt a little embarrassed, but her father said the trophies belonged there.

Back home, in the privacy of her bedroom, she placed the trophies on her shelf and was happy. She had always earned honors because of her brains. But winning in sports was a new experience. She thanked her tired thumb. "You did it, thumb. You made me champion." As its reward, Lupe went to the bathroom and filled the bathroom sink with warm water. She let her thumb swim and splash as it pleased. Then she climbed into bed and drifted into a hard-won sleep. END

| Words to Know! | **commotion** | noisy, excited activity |

Story Elements

Setting

1. **CIRCLE** Where does Lupe's family go to celebrate?

Character

2. **UNDERLINE** How does Lupe feel about the attention she gets at the restaurant?

Theme

3. ✔ **CHECK** Which is a theme of this story?

   ❑ Parents should never encourage their children.
   ❑ If you work hard, you can achieve a goal.
   ❑ You cannot win by being nice.
   ❑ More people should play marbles.

▶ Now go to page 149. Complete Part 3 of the chart and the theme.

Skills Check

1. **BOX** Mark a sentence that shows that Lupe is proud of herself.

2. ▶ **WRITE** How does Lupe solve her problem?

_____

_____

_____

Active Reading

WRITE What "awful problem" does the poem's narrator have with basketball?

_____

_____

Craft and Structure

Text Structure: Stanza A stanza is a group of one or more lines about one idea or topic. A stanza in a poem is like a paragraph in a story.

1. **CIRCLE** Circle each stanza in this poem.

2. **WRITE** What is the first stanza about?

_____

_____

_____

_____

React and Write

WRITE Do you think this poem is humorous or serious? Use details from the poem to explain your response.

S·T·R·E·T·C·H

by Gordon Korman & Bernice Korman

Basketball is everything!
It's always been my dream
To deke and sky and dunk and fly,
And play for my school team.

But there's an awful problem
No one can seem to fix:
The team height starts at six foot four,
And I am four foot six.

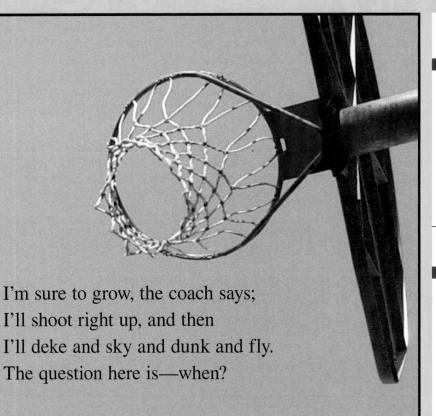

I'm sure to grow, the coach says;
I'll shoot right up, and then
I'll deke and sky and dunk and fly.
The question here is—when?

It might take till I'm thirty,
That's what I greatly fear,
For I'll no longer be in school—
(Miss Mott says I'll be here.)

I've got to do some growing
(Is there a stretching pill?),
I won't be here at thirty!
(Miss Mott says yes, I will.)

I shall not be discouraged,
I'll never shut the door.
Someday when I sit on the bench
My feet will reach the floor!

I'll make it to the court, then,
To play for my school team.
I'll deke and sky and dunk and fly—
It's always been my dream. **END**

 Craft and Structure

Rhyme Two or more words rhyme when they end with the same sound or with similar sounds.

BOX Mark pairs of words that rhyme at the ends of the lines in this poem.

 Craft and Structure

Speaker A poem's speaker is a character that the poet creates to tell the story.

UNDERLINE Mark four details that the speaker of this poem shares about himself or herself.

 Cross-Text Analysis

▶ **WRITE** How is the speaker of this poem similar to Lupe in "The Marble Champ"?

_____

_____

_____

_____

_____

_____

Word Challenge

start

1 **Identify them.** Which activities take a lot of **energy**?

☐ sleeping
☐ running
☐ blinking
☐ swimming

3 Multiple-Meaning Words

Multiple-meaning words have more than one meaning. Example: A *goal* is a place where you must put the ball to score points in a game. A *goal* is also something that you want to do or achieve.

My **goal** is to put the ball in the **goal**.

Read each sentence. Then check the correct meaning of *energy* in that sentence.

I ate a snack. Now I have **energy** for practice.

☐ strength   ☐ time   ☐ electricity

Leaving the lights on is a waste of **energy**.

☐ strength   ☐ time   ☐ electricity

2 **Decide.** Which would **strengthen** a friendship?

☐ helping a friend study
☐ talking behind a friend's back
☐ giving a gift to a friend
☐ ignoring a friend

4 **Tell about it.** What do you **rely** on each person for?

A good friend: _____

Your parents: _____

Police: _____

5

Decide. Put a **Y** next to each **display** you would want to see. Put an **N** next to any **display** you would *not* want to see.

____ a stamp collection

____ the latest sports cars

____ movie star posters

____ a shoe collection

____ dinosaur bones

6

Name them. To get an **accurate** weight, you would use a

_____

To get an **accurate** temperature, you would use a

_____

To get an **accurate** height, you would use a

_____

7

Think about it. Complete each sentence.

If there's a fire, **proceed** to the nearest

_____

If you hit a baseball, **proceed** to

_____

When you get to school, **proceed** to your _____

8   Word Families

This took **courage**. I'm glad you **encouraged** me!

A **word family** is a group of words that share the same base word and have related meanings, such as *courage*, *encourage*, and *discourage*. *Courage* means "bravery" or "strength." *Encourage* means "to give someone praise or support." *Discourage* means "to take away someone's confidence."

Complete each sentence with the correct form of *courage*.

1. It takes _____ to stick up for what you believe in.

2. The coach gave a pep talk to _____ us before the big game.

3. I want to try snowboarding, but my parents think it's too dangerous. They keep trying to _____ me.

9

Complete them. Complete the sentences with **opponents** and **previous**.

My soccer team is getting ready for the big game.

Our _____ won their _____

game. But we're pretty sure we can beat them.

10

Circle one in each row. Would you feel **exhaustion** from . . .

walking **OR** running?

staying awake **OR** sleeping?

watching TV **OR** studying?

gym class **OR** music class?

 finish

Writing Text Type

Literary Analysis

In a **literary analysis**, the writer discusses the characters, plot, or setting of a story.

▶ **Read Anand Gupta's analysis of the plot of "The Marble Champ."**

Introduction

An **introductory statement** identifies the story's text type, title, and author.

1. UNDERLINE the **introductory statement**.

A **focus statement** presents a controlling idea about the story's characters, plot, or setting.

2. BOX the **focus statement**.

Body

Each body paragraph starts with a **topic sentence**.

Details, **quotes**, and **examples** support the topic sentence.

3. ✔CHECK two **supporting details** in each body paragraph.

Language Use

Linking words and **phrases** connect ideas.

4. CIRCLE five **linking phrases**.

Direct quotations from the story support the writer's ideas.

5. DOUBLE UNDERLINE two direct quotations.

Conclusion

The **conclusion** sums up or restates the focus statement.

6. ★STAR the conclusion.

Student Model

A Story With a Winning Plot
by Anand Gupta

Gary Soto's short story "The Marble Champ" has a suspenseful plot. The story follows as the main character, Lupe, struggles to succeed at the one thing she cannot do well: play sports.

Interest builds as Lupe gives herself a huge challenge, then strives to meet it. At first, Lupe believes she will never be good at sports. However, she dreams of a sports award. She thinks, "I wish I could win something, anything, even marbles." (152) Lupe decides to enter a marble contest. She practices daily. She does exercises to strengthen her thumb. In fact, Lupe works so hard that her parents worry.

On contest day, there are many exciting events. Lupe beats many opponents easily and makes it to the finals. Crowds watch and cheer as Lupe becomes the marble champion.

At the story's end, Lupe is proud because she has met the challenge she gave herself. "She thanks her tired thumb. 'You did it, thumb. You made me champion.'" (163) This story has an exciting plot with a happy ending.

Analyze the Text Type

▶ **Work with a partner to understand the purpose and form of a literary analysis.**

Purpose: Literary Analysis

The purpose of a literary analysis is _____
_____

Introduction

The **introductory paragraph** includes:

1. an introductory statement that identifies _____
_____

2. a focus statement that presents _____ about the story.

Student Model | In his introduction, Anand

1. identifies the text type, title, and author of the story, which are:
_____

2. includes a focus statement with this controlling idea: _____
_____

Body

The **body paragraphs** give supporting details, quotes, and examples.

1. Each body paragraph starts with a _____
2. Details, quotes, and examples _____ the topic sentence.

Student Model

1. The topic sentence of the first body paragraph is _____
_____

2. List two details Anand includes in his first body paragraph.

- _____
- _____

Conclusion

The **conclusion** sums up or restates the _____

Student Model | Anand's conclusion states that _____
_____

Brainstorm

▶ Read the writing prompt. Then use the idea web to help you brainstorm details and ideas about the story.

Characters

Plot

Writing Prompt:
Analyze character, plot, or setting in "The Marble Champ."

Setting

Choose Your Topic

▶ Select one of your ideas from the web. Then complete the sentence.

I am going to examine the story's _____

because _____

_____

Organize Ideas for Writing

► **Complete this outline with notes for your literary analysis.**

I. Introduction List information about the story you will analyze.

A. Text Type: _____

B. Title: _____

C. Author: _____

D. I will analyze the story's _____

E. The controlling idea I will focus on is _____

_____

II. Body Write a topic sentence for each body paragraph that supports
the focus statement. List two details that support each topic sentence.

A. Topic Sentence _____

_____

Detail 1: _____

_____

Detail 2: _____

_____

B. Topic Sentence _____

_____

Detail 1: _____

_____

Detail 2: _____

_____

III. Conclusion In one or two sentences, restate the focus statement.

_____

_____

_____

_____

Write Your Draft

▶ Write a draft of your literary analysis.

Writing Prompt:
Write a literary analysis that discusses the characters, plot, or setting of "The Marble Champ."

WORD CHOICES	
Everyday	**Precise**
try	attempt, strive
look at	inspect
get better	improve

_____ (title)

Introduction

▶ **Write your introductory statement.**

The _____ by _____
(text type and reading title)   (author's name)

is about _____
(state topic)

▶ **Write your focus statement or plan.**

The story's _____

_____

_____

▶ Type your introductory paragraph on the computer or write it on paper. Then use these linking words and phrases to help you complete a draft of your literary analysis.

Body

The story takes place in . . .	The details help to . . .
The main character acts . . .	The events are . . .
Other characters do . . .	The language builds . . .

Conclusion

Overall, . . .	In conclusion, . . .
At the end of the story, . . .	The story is memorable because . . .

Revise Your Essay

▶ **Evaluate:** Rate your literary analysis. Then have a writing partner rate it.

Scoring Guide

needs improvement	average	good	excellent
1	2	3	4

1. **UNDERLINE** the introductory statement. Does it give the story's text type, title, and author?

   Self   1   2   3   4

   Partner   1   2   3   4

2. BOX the focus statement. Does it include a controlling idea?

   Self   1   2   3   4

   Partner   1   2   3   4

3. **UNDERLINE** the topic sentence in each body paragraph. Do they support the focus statement?

   Self   1   2   3   4

   Partner   1   2   3   4

4. ✔**CHECK** details, quotes, and examples in each body paragraph. Do they support the writer's ideas?

   Self   1   2   3   4

   Partner   1   2   3   4

5. CIRCLE linking words and phrases. Do they connect ideas?

   Self   1   2   3   4

   Partner   1   2   3   4

6. ★**STAR** the conclusion. Does it sum up the focus statement?

   Self   1   2   3   4

   Partner   1   2   3   4

▶ **Discuss:** Give feedback on your partner's literary analysis.

1. Start with a positive comment about your partner's essay.

   Your introduction is effective because

   _____

   You support your focus statement well

   by _____

   _____

2. Give your partner suggestions for revision.

   I have a question about _____

   _____

   This sentence would be clearer if

   _____

3. Answer any questions your partner has about your suggestions.

4. Ask your partner for feedback. Use the frames below to summarize your partner's feedback.

   I did an effective job of . . .
   You liked the way I . . .
   You had a question about . . .
   My essay needs . . .

▶ **Revise:** Now revise your literary analysis.

Grammar SUBJECT-VERB AGREEMENT

The **subject and verb** in a sentence must agree in number.

- A verb that agrees with a **singular subject** tells what one person, place, or thing is doing. It usually ends in *-s* or *-es*.
- A verb that agrees with a **plural subject** tells what more than one person or thing is doing. It usually does not end in *-s* or *-es*.

Example

Singular Subject	Plural Subject
The **marble** rolls across the ground.	The **marbles** roll across the ground.
Lupe squeezes an eraser.	**We** squeeze erasers, too.

▶ **Put an X next to the sentence if it has subject-verb agreement errors. Put a check if the sentence is correct.**

1. Sometimes, Lupe kick the ball into her own goal. ___X___

2. She rides a bike with training wheels. _____

3. Every day, Lupe practice shooting marbles on her bed. _____

4. Her muscles burns from exhaustion. _____

5. Her brother and father gives her some hints. _____

6. Lupe enters the marble championship. _____

▶ **Rewrite the following sentences with correct subject-verb agreement. (Be sure to keep all the sentences in present tense.)**

7. Several girls follows Lupe from game to game.

_____

8. Lupe's father cheer for her.

_____

9. Miss Baseball Cap stare at the ground.

_____

10. Lupe win the game against the boys' champ.

_____

▶ **Edit Your Draft.** Look at each sentence in your draft. **Do all the subjects and verbs agree?** Fix any that do not.

Mechanics USING POSSESSIVE NOUNS

A **possessive noun** shows ownership.

- Add an apostrophe (') and an -*s* to a singular noun.
- Add an apostrophe to a plural noun that ends in -*s*.

Example

Correct	Incorrect
Lupe's brother gave her advice.	Lupes brother gave her advice.
She looked at the marbles' colors.	She looked at the marbles colors.

▶ **Find and correct five errors in this paragraph.**

Student Model

Lupe is a strong character because she struggle to be a sports champion. She decides to start playing marbels. She works very hard at it. Lupes muscles begin to hurt from all the exercises that she does. Finally, Lupe wins against a tough oponnent after listening to her fathers' advice.

CHECK AND CORRECT

- ❑ **UNDERLINE** and correct two errors with possessive nouns.
- ❑ Correct one subject-verb agreement error.
- ❑ CIRCLE and correct two spelling errors.

▶ **Edit Your Draft.** Look at the sentences in your draft. **Are all the possessive nouns formed correctly?** Fix any that are not.

Final Draft/Present

▶ **Write a final draft of your paragraph on the computer or on paper. Recheck it and correct any errors before you present it.**

Focus Skill · Analyze Information

Use a Seating Chart

People use a seating chart when they buy tickets. It is also helpful to look at the chart to find your seat at a sports event.

▶ **Read the seating chart and answer the questions below.**

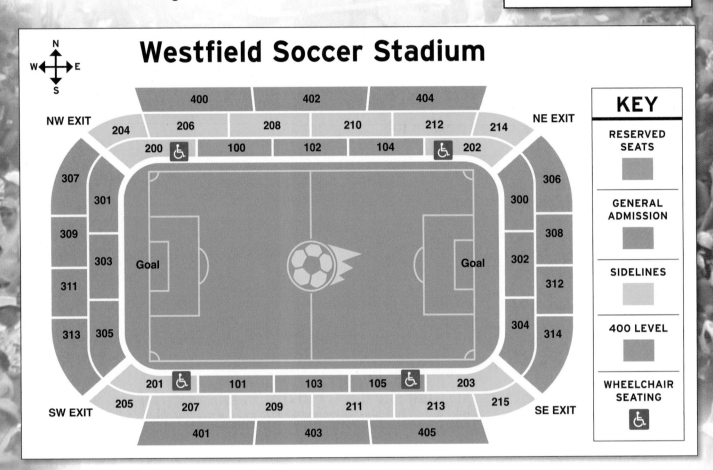

Westfield Soccer Stadium

❶ **Which sections would give you a good view of the entire field?**

Ⓐ 302 and 304   Ⓒ 214 and 215

Ⓑ 102 and 103   Ⓓ 301 and 303

❷ **Where is reserved wheelchair seating available?**

Ⓐ section 105 only   Ⓒ sections 105 and 201

Ⓑ section 201 only   Ⓓ sections 200 and 202

❸ **In which section do seats probably cost least?**

Ⓐ Reserved Seats   Ⓒ Wheelchair Seating

Ⓑ Sidelines   Ⓓ 400 Level

Explain your response.

_____

_____

_____

Sports Referee
T.C. Cameron

Meet a referee whose calls decide the game.

▶ **Read the interview and job information. Then answer the questions below about T.C. Cameron's job.**

S **Scholastic: How do you make a difficult call during a game?**

I try to get as close to the action as possible so I can see what is going on. If I'm not 100% sure, I look at players' behavior. Usually, if a player messes up, he or she looks down and walks away from the play.

S **What makes someone a good referee?**

T.C.: You need to have two sides to your personality. Mostly, you are in the background. But when you have to make a call, all eyes are on you. You have to pay very close attention. If there is a conflict, you have to defend the call you made. The athletes, coaches, and fans depend on you for a fair game.

S **Do you ever make mistakes?**

I do, and I learn from them, just like players and coaches do.

ON THE JOB

LOCATION

Annapolis, Maryland

EDUCATION

Bachelor's degree in Journalism

RESPONSIBILITIES

• Makes calls during a game
• Works with players and coaches to call a fair game

SKILLS

• Paying close attention
• Making judgments

SALARY

Experienced referees make $30,000–$250,000.

FAVORITE PART OF THE JOB

"I enjoy walking off the field knowing that each team had a fair game."

CAREER CONNECTION

Hospitality and Tourism
www.careerclusters.org

Related Jobs
• sports league organizer
• coach
• athletic trainer

❶ **What information does T.C. use to decide a play?**

_____

_____

❷ **How difficult do you think a referee's job is? Mark the line.**

1   2   3   4   5
Not very difficult   **Very difficult**

❸ **I think the toughest part of a sports referee's job is** _____

_____

_____

Focus Skills | Set Criteria | Take Notes

What makes a champion?

Hold a class debate about what makes a true champion. Which is more important: winning, or being a good sport?

❶ **Gather examples.** How does Lupe act like a champion? List one or two examples. What athletes do you consider true champions, and why? List one or two examples.

- Lupe is a champion _because she works so hard to improve._

- Lupe also _____

- _____ is a sports champion _because_

  _____

- _____ is a sports champion _because_

  _____

❷ **Set criteria.** How do champions behave? Rate these qualities of a sports champ in order of importance from 1 (most important) to 6 (least important).

Winning the Game	Being a Good Sport
_____ **Skill:** being good at the sport	_____ **Fairness:** playing by the rules
_____ **Training:** practicing in order to improve	_____ **Sportsmanship:** treating opponents with respect
_____ **Bravery:** taking risks and facing challenges	_____ **Teamwork:** being a team player

❸ **State your position.** What does it mean to be a champion? Does a champion always win? Is a champion always a good sport? Write your definition:

A champion is someone who _____

_____

_____

④ **Prepare for your debate.** Write a strong opening statement. Add facts and examples to support your ideas. Then think ahead: How might the other team respond to your ideas? Organize your notes, and hold your debate!

AN EFFECTIVE DEBATE

✓ is calm and polite, even when feelings are strong.

✓ supports ideas with facts and examples.

✓ plans out responses to claims from the other side.

DEBATE: What makes a champion?
_____

OPENING STATEMENT: _____
_____
_____
_____

OUR SIDE:

a. _____
_____
_____
_____

b. _____
_____
_____
_____

c. _____
_____
_____
_____

THE OTHER SIDE:

a. _____
_____
_____
_____

b. _____
_____
_____
_____

c. _____
_____
_____
_____

CLOSING STATEMENT: In conclusion, we believe that **winning the game /**
being a good sport (circle one) is what makes a champion, because
_____
_____

Comprehension

▶ **Fill in the circle next to the correct answer.**

1. In the story, what is Lupe's main problem?

   &Ⓐ She is doing poorly in school.

   Ⓑ She has an important race coming up.

   Ⓒ She has not had any success in sports.

   Ⓓ She has a sore thumb.

2. Evaluate: Lupe succeeds because she
_____.

CRITICAL READING

   Ⓐ takes lessons from a marbles expert

   Ⓑ sets a goal and works hard to reach it

   Ⓒ reads about marbles and other sports

   Ⓓ cheats as she plays in the big marbles contest

3. Which pair of words best describes Lupe?

   Ⓐ sad and angry

   Ⓑ smart and determined

   Ⓒ lazy and content

   Ⓓ mean and afraid

4. Synthesize: Which will most likely happen in the future?

CRITICAL READING

   Ⓐ Lupe will continue to play marbles.

   Ⓑ Lupe will become a great soccer player.

   Ⓒ Lupe will fail some classes in school.

   Ⓓ Lupe will never play a sport again.

5. What is the theme of the story?

   Ⓐ It is hard to learn how to play marbles.

   Ⓑ Brothers and sisters should work together.

   Ⓒ Friendship is more important than winning.

   Ⓓ If you work hard, you can achieve a goal.

Here's a Tip.
Check your work against the reading you're being tested on. Make sure your answer agrees with what's in the reading.

Vocabulary

▶ **Fill in the circle next to the correct definition of the underlined word.**

1. Lupe's aim grew more <u>accurate</u> with practice.
   - Ⓐ lazy
   - Ⓑ exact
   - Ⓒ difficult
   - Ⓓ large

2. She did exercises to <u>strengthen</u> her muscles.
   - Ⓐ make more powerful
   - Ⓑ lengthen
   - Ⓒ wave
   - Ⓓ make smaller

3. Lupe's <u>opponent</u> was also a good marbles player.
   - Ⓐ family member
   - Ⓑ director of a contest
   - Ⓒ teammate
   - Ⓓ person to compete with

▶ **Choose the correct definition for the underlined multiple-meaning word.**

4. While she practiced, Lupe ate a snack for <u>energy</u>.
   - Ⓐ electricity
   - Ⓑ rest
   - Ⓒ strength
   - Ⓓ lunch

▶ **Choose the correct word from the word family.**

5. Lupe's family gave her a lot of _____.
   - Ⓐ encourage
   - Ⓑ courageous
   - Ⓒ discourage
   - Ⓓ encouragement

Short Answer

CRITICAL READING

▶ **Synthesize:** Use what you have read in this Workshop to answer the question. Check your spelling and grammar.

How would you describe the character Lupe Medrano?

_____

_____

_____

_____

WORKSHOP 7

INFORMATIONAL TEXT

COMPREHENSION FOCUS
Cause and Effect

CRITICAL READING FOCUS
Analyze
Synthesize
Evaluate

Reading 1 Pet Tiger Attack | **News Article**

Reading 2 Wild Pets | **Magazine Article**

Reading 3 Zoos Go Wild! | **Science Text**

Taming Wild Beasts

Wild animals are at home in jungles, swamps, and open plains. But some wild animals live in zoos. Some even live in people's homes—as pets!

Are animals ever happy outside of the wild? Can wild beasts ever be tamed? Turn the page to find out.

Target Word

▶ Read the Target Words. Rate each one using the scale below.*

Meaning

▶ Read the Target Word meanings. Write in the missing words.

Examples

▶ Finish the Target Word examples below. Write in the missing ones.

Target Word	Meaning	Examples
threat (p. 184) *threat* (noun) ① ② ③ ④	a _____ that something bad might _____	• _____ are a **threat** to my safety. • _____ _____
enormous (p. 184) *e•nor•mous* (adjective) ① ② ③ ④	very large	• _____ _____ are **enormous** animals. • _____ _____
capture (p. 184) *cap•ture* (verb) ① ② ③ ④	to _____ a person, animal, or place by _____	• I would like to **capture** that _____ _____ • _____ _____
fierce (p. 187) *fierce* (adjective) ① ② ③ ④	violent and _____ _____	A lion that is chasing its prey is **fierce**.
habitat (p. 192) *hab•i•tat* (noun) ① ② ③ ④	the natural environment of a plant or animal	• Some **habitats** in the United States include _____ _____ • _____ _____

The Key Idea

▶ **WRITE** What is this article mostly about?

_____

_____

VOCABULARY
Target Word

remove

re•move (verb)

Rate It: ① ② ③ ④

Meaning

to _____

Example

Someone might **remove** an unwelcome animal from a yard by _____

_____

React and Write

▶ **WRITE** Do you think the police were right to take away the tiger? Why or why not?

Summarize

In one or two sentences, summarize what happened after Ming bit Antoine Yates. Include the topic and important details.

Pet Tiger Attack
New York Man Bitten by His Pet

Ming the tiger was living in an apartment.

October 4—Many people keep pets in their homes. But yesterday, Antoine Yates's pet was **removed** by the police. That's because the pet was a 450-pound tiger! Yates says the tiger is his best friend. But the police said it was a threat to the neighborhood.

Yates bought the tiger as a tiny cub. Tiger cubs are fuzzy and cute. So it's easy to see why someone might want one. Yates named his cub Ming. He fed Ming from a baby bottle. They wrestled and played together.

But soon, Ming grew to his enormous adult size. Playing with him became dangerous! One day, Ming chomped on Yates's arm and leg.

Yates had to go to the hospital. But he didn't want to get Ming in trouble. So he told the doctors that a dog bit him. The doctors doubted Yates. He got nervous and ran off. That made the doctors call the police.

As a result, the police broke into Yates's home. They captured Ming. Then they transported him to a wild animal shelter. Yates misses his pet. But police and neighbors think Ming is where he belongs. END

Words to Know! | **doubt** to not believe something

Comprehension Focus

Cause and Effect

A **cause** is the reason something happens. An **effect** is the result of a cause.
To find cause and effect:

- Ask yourself "Why did it happen?" to find the cause.
- Ask yourself "What happened?" to find the effect.
- Look for signal words or phrases such as *because*, *so*, *as a result*,
  therefore, and *for this reason*.

▶ **Complete the chart with the cause-and-effect relationships in
  "Pet Tiger Attack."**

Cause

_____

_____

_____

_____

_____

Effect

_____

_____

_____

_____

_____

Cause

_____

_____

_____

_____

_____

Effect

_____

_____

_____

_____

_____

The Key Idea

▶ **WRITE** What is this article mostly about?

_____

_____

VOCABULARY
Target Word

concerned

con•cerned (adjective)

Rate It: ① ② ③ ④

Meaning

_____ or anxious

Example

Neighbors might *be*

concerned that a pet alligator

would _____

_____

React and Write

▶ **WRITE** What if *your* neighbor owned a pet alligator? How would you feel about that?

WILD PETS

Do wild animals make good pets? One man thought so. But the law said no.

Many people like pets that are furry and cuddly. But John Boyko loves pets that are scaly and cold. He and his wife had three alligators!

The Gator Family

The Boykos got their first two alligators as babies. Later, they met a man who had an alligator he didn't want. In fact, the man was planning to have his vet kill it! So the Boykos rescued it.

The Boykos loved their alligators dearly. They played with their pets and took them for rides in the car. They even took the alligators to visit family. "We didn't have kids," said John Boyko. "We had gators."

John Boyko gets ready to take his pet alligators for a ride.

Afraid of Alligators

To John Boyko, his alligators were like any other pets. But his neighbors were **concerned**. In fact, they were terrified! Neighbor Margie Branca was afraid for her children. That's because alligators can be really fierce. "A dog bites you and backs off," Branca said. "An alligator bites you to eat you."

In time, some neighbors complained. As a result, the police came to the Boykos' house. They captured the alligators. They took the alligators away to a zoo.

The zookeeper said that the alligators were in good shape. He said that the Boykos "did a good job caring for the animals." John Boyko was mad! Like the zookeeper said, he knew that he was a good pet owner. So he felt he deserved to keep his pets. ➤

Words to Know!	**terrified** really scared

Cause and Effect

1. **UNDERLINE** Why did the Boykos have to rescue an alligator?

2. **WRITE** Why was neighbor Margie Branca terrified?

3. **WRITE** What happened when the neighbors complained about the alligators?

CRITICAL READING

Synthesize

WRITE If you were John Boyko, what would you do to try to get your alligators back?

A boy plays with his wild pet snake.

Active Reading

UNDERLINE Why are some wild pets in danger?

VOCABULARY
Target Word

legal

le•gal (adjective)

Rate It: ① ② ③ ④

Meaning

having to do with the _____

Example

It is **legal** to keep _____

_____ as pets.

React and Write

▶ **WRITE** Do you think people should be allowed to keep wild pets? Why or why not?

Summarize

In one or two sentences, summarize the topic and important details in "Pets in Danger."

Pets in Danger

Should John Boyko and others be allowed to have wild pets? Some experts insist that almost nobody can handle a wild pet. Taking care of wild animals is costly—and hard. Often, they need expensive food and lots of exercise. And when they grow up, they can become a threat to their owners.

Because wild pets are so difficult, many owners abandon them. Then the pets end up in shelters, and the shelters get really crowded. As a result, some animals are even put to sleep.

Pets and the Law

States want to protect wild animals—by leaving them in the wild. That's why many states ban wild pets.

But wild pet owners say their pets should be **legal**. After all, this is America! People should have the right to choose the pets they like. Besides, many owners take good care of their wild pets.

In 2003, officials gave John Boyko 30 days to find a new home for his gators. Just as time was running out, he was able to move them to a private home in another state. Boyko promised to keep his pets safe. Are they still safe? Who knows? END

Words to Know!	**abandon** to leave something you are responsible for

Comprehension Focus

Cause and Effect

▶ **Complete this chart with cause-and-effect relationships in "Wild Pets."**

Cause

_____

_____

_____

_____

_____

Effect

_____

_____

_____

_____

_____

Cause

_____

_____

_____

_____

_____

Effect

_____

_____

_____

_____

_____

The Key Idea

▶ **WRITE** What is this article mostly about?

_____

_____

Target Word

range

range (noun)

Rate It: ① ② ③ ④

Meaning

the areas where _____

_____

Example

_____

have large home **ranges**.

React and Write

▶ **WRITE** Would you like to live in a zoo? Yes or no? Explain your answer.

ZOOS GO WILD!

Would you get bored living in a cage? Animals at the zoo do. How can zoos keep animals happy?

Gus the polar bear checks out two zoo visitors.

The Bored Bear

Today, Gus the polar bear is a star. He lives at the Central Park Zoo in New York City. Kids love to come watch him swim and play. But Gus wasn't always so much fun. Back in 1994, he had a problem. He would swim laps for hours without stopping. Gus wasn't sick. He wasn't losing his mind, either. Gus did laps because he was so *bored*!

Gus was not alone. Many zoo animals are bored and unhappy. That's because they prefer the wild. In the wild, animals roam in packs. They hunt, play, and fight. In other words, they have things to do.

Home on the Range

Zoo experts are aware of this problem. They study animals' lives in the wild. They try to figure out what zoo animals are missing. Often, animals that are unhappy in a zoo have large "home **ranges**" in the wild. A home range is the area where a wild animal lives and roams.

Polar bears have huge home ranges. In the wild, they have a range of up to 31,000 miles a year. They also hunt for seals on the ice. Zoo cages are tiny compared with the wild. As a result, a polar bear like Gus gets restless. He has nowhere to roam and no seals to hunt.

Lions and tigers also have big home ranges. In the wild, they roam around and hunt for both larger and smaller animals. So, like polar bears, they get bored in the zoo.

Other animals do better in zoos. Snow leopards have small home ranges. Because of this, they may become less bored by zoo life. ➤

Words to Know! **roam** to travel

Cause and Effect

1. UNDERLINE Find the sentence that tells why Gus swam laps for hours.

2. ▷ WRITE Why don't polar bears do well in zoos?

_____

_____

3. ▷ WRITE Why might snow leopards be happier in zoos?

_____

_____

_____

REVIEW
Problem and Solution

CIRCLE Find the sentence that describes the main problem with putting polar bears in cages.

CRITICAL READING
Analyze

▷ WRITE According to the text, what could zoos do to make polar bears, lions, and tigers happier?

_____

_____

_____

_____

Active Reading

★**STAR** What animal has a zoo home built like the Congo forest?

VOCABULARY
Target Word

exhibit

ex•hib•it *(noun)*

Rate It: ① ② ③ ④

Meaning

a display in a _____

where people can _____ it

Example

_____

might *be* in an **exhibit** of American animals.

React and Write

▶**WRITE** What zoo animal would you like to learn more about? Tell why.

Summarize

▶**WRITE** Summarize the topic and important details in the science text "Zoos Go Wild!"

Gus's New Home

Gus's zookeepers wanted to help him out. So they rebuilt his home. Now his **exhibit** is more like his natural habitat. Pumps move the water around in his tank. And Gus has a snow bank to keep himself cool.

The zookeepers have also made Gus's life more interesting. Gus loves to eat fish. In the old days, the zoo just gave it to him. But now Gus has to work for his dinner.

The zoo freezes his fish in ice. Then, they bury it in some gravel. Gus has to find it before he can eat it. He also has to remove the fish from the ice.

Gus's new home is working out well. He swims laps less often now. He doesn't seem so bored. And kids love to visit him.

TEXT FEATURE Reading a Map

Bronx Zoo Congo Gorilla Forest

Mandrill Forest · Gorilla Encounter · Great Gorilla Forest · Okapi Jungle · Walk-Thru Fallen Tree · Gorilla Forest Overlook · Congo Gift Shop · Forest Edge View · Rain Forest Trail · Entry

No More Bars

Gus isn't the only animal with a new cage. Today, many zoos are "going wild."

The Bronx Zoo in New York spent thirteen years designing and building a better home for gorillas. The new exhibit was built to seem like the Congo forest. As a result, the gorillas are surrounded by trees and waterfalls. From inside a glass tunnel, visitors can see a band of gorillas at play.

At the San Diego Zoo, enormous elephants, tall giraffes, and fierce rhinos roam freely in a huge animal park. People can see them from behind barriers, or from an open-air train. It feels like an African safari!

Zoos are getting good results from their new exhibits. The animals seem happier. And more people visit. Zoos are now more fun for everyone. (END)

Words to Know!	**safari** a trip taken to see wild animals

A map is a detailed plan of a place. It shows where things are in relation to each other.

❶ Where do you think the gorillas live?

Ⓐ the Congo Gift Shop   Ⓒ the Okapi Jungle

Ⓑ the Great Gorilla Forest   Ⓓ the Entry

❷ What would a visitor pass while walking between the Mandrill Forest and the Rain Forest Trail?

Ⓐ the Gorilla Forest Overlook   Ⓒ the Walk-Thru Fallen Tree

Ⓑ the Forest Edge View   Ⓓ the Congo Gift Shop

❸ **Analyze:** Which place on the map would you most like to see? Why?

_____

_____

Cause and Effect

1. **UNDERLINE** Gus got a new cage. Find two things that changed for Gus as a result.

2. ▷ **WRITE** Why does Gus have more fun eating fish now?

_____

_____

CRITICAL READING
Evaluate

▷ **WRITE** Based on the text, do you believe that changes at zoos are helping animals? Explain.

_____

_____

_____

✓ Skills Check

1. (CIRCLE) Why are the gorillas at the Bronx Zoo surrounded by trees now?

2. ▷ **WRITE** What are two effects of new zoo designs?

• _____

_____

• _____

_____

VOCABULARY

WordChallenge

start

1 Check two. Which looks could make someone seem **fierce**?

- ☐ a smile
- ☐ a frown
- ☐ a snarl
- ☐ a wink

2 Multiple-Meaning Words

Multiple-meaning words have more than one meaning. For example, a *bat* is a small mammal that flies at night. A *bat* is also what a baseball player uses to hit baseballs.

Look up the word *range* in the glossary. Below, mark all correct definitions for *range*.

- ☐ The area where an animal lives and roams.
- ☐ A line of mountains.
- ☐ Strange and unusual things in a movie.
- ☐ A variety of a group of things.

3 Name them. Name three items that are part of your **habitat**.

- _____
- _____
- _____

A human teen's habitat.

4 Rate them. Which **threats** are you **concerned** about? Write **N** for **not concerned**. Write **C** for **concerned**.

____ an earthquake   ____ a shark attack

____ lightning   ____ a mean neighbor

____ aliens from outer space   ____ being chased by a lion

5 Complete them. Finish each sentence.

A police officer **captures** _____

A cat might **capture** _____

A fishing rod **captures** _____

6 **Evaluate them.** These are possible slogans for a new ice cream store. Rate them from 1 (best) to 4 (worst).

____ "We serve small scoops of ice cream on **enormous** cones!"

____ "We sell **enormous** scoops of ice cream for a small price!"

____ "We sell small scoops of ice cream at **enormous** prices!"

____ "We sell **enormous** scoops of ice cream at **enormous** prices!"

7 **Finish it.** Complete this sentence with **habitats** and **exhibits**.

At the Bronx Zoo, you can see animals

in _____ that are a lot like the

animals' natural _____.

8 Verb Endings

 I **flip** through the air with ease! A minute ago, I **flipped** three times.

A **verb ending** can be added to a verb to show when an action takes place. To show that an action happened in the past, you can often add *-ed*. To show that an action is happening in the present, you can often add *-ing*.

Yesterday, I *played*. Today, I am *playing*.

Add the verb. Use the correct verb ending.

1. Last week, we _____ a lost bird. **(capture)**

2. No, I'm not done yet. I'm still _____ my homework. **(finish)**

3. After they _____ the cast from my arm, I was able to play baseball again. **(remove)**

9 **Think about it.** Decide if each animal should be **legal** to own as a pet.

	should be legal	should *not* be legal
polar bear	☐	☐
dolphin	☐	☐
rat	☐	☐
duck	☐	☐

10 **Imagine it.** What would happen if . . .

• one tire were **removed** from a car?

_____

• one whisker were **removed** from a sleeping tiger?

_____

• all the teeth were **removed** from your mouth?

_____

 ○finish

Writing Text Type
Opinion Essay

An **opinion essay** states an opinion about an issue or topic. The writer supports the opinion with reasons, examples, and facts.

► **Read student Michael Wong's opinion essay about elephants in the circus.**

Student Model

Introduction

An **introductory statement** introduces the issue.

1. <u>UNDERLINE</u> the **introductory statement**.

The introductory paragraph also includes a clear **focus statement** that states the writer's opinion.

2. BOX the **focus statement**.

Body

Each body paragraph begins with a **topic sentence** about the issue.

3. <u>UNDERLINE</u> the **topic sentence** in each body paragraph.

Reasons, facts, and examples support the topic sentence.

4. ✔CHECK three supporting **reasons, facts, or examples**.

Language Use

Linking words and phrases introduce or connect ideas.

5. CIRCLE four **linking words or phrases**.

Conclusion

The **conclusion** restates the opinion and offers a recommendation for readers.

6. ★STAR the **conclusion**.

The Case Against Circus Elephants
by Michael Wong

It is unfair to use elephants as performers in the circus. Removing an elephant from the wild and forcing it to learn circus acts is wrong.

First of all, a circus cannot provide a natural habitat for an elephant. An elephant needs to roam freely in a large, open space. Circus trainers often lock elephants in small, hot cages for long periods of time. This practice is cruel.

Second, circus life does not meet elephants' social needs. Elephants are naturally social. In the wild, they roam in herds, and play with other elephants. A circus elephant may see another elephant only rarely, or never. Instead, they work for hours every day to learn and perform circus acts. It is inhumane to take elephants from life in a herd and force them to entertain people instead.

In conclusion, elephants belong in the wild, not in a circus. I urge everyone to boycott any circus that uses elephants as entertainment.

Analyze the Text Type

▶ **Work with a partner to understand the purpose and form of an opinion essay.**

Purpose: Opinion Essay
The purpose of an opinion essay is to _____ _____

Introduction

The **introductory paragraph** of an opinion essay:

1. introduces _____

2. includes _____ that gives the writer's opinion about the issue.

Student Model In his introduction, Michael:

1. introduces the topic as _____

2. includes a clear focus statement, which is: _____ _____

Body

1. Each body paragraph starts with _____

2. _____ support the topic sentence.

Student Model

1. The topic sentence for Michael's first paragraph is _____ _____

2. One fact that Michael includes in his first body paragraph is _____ _____

Conclusion

The **conclusion** restates _____

and _____

_____

Student Model Michael concludes his opinion essay by recommending that _____ _____

Brainstorm

▶ Read the writing prompt. Then use the boxes to brainstorm ideas.

Writing Prompt:
Is it humane to keep wild animals in zoos? Write an essay stating your opinion.

Yes! Zoos are humane.

No! Zoos are not humane.

State Your Opinion

▶ Use your ideas from the idea web to help you determine your opinion.

My opinion is that it is _____ to keep wild animals in zoos,

because _____

_____

Organize Ideas for Writing

▶ **Complete this outline with notes for your opinion essay.**

   I. Introduction Introduce the issue and your opinion about it.

      A. Issue: _____

      _____

      B. My opinion: _____

      _____

      _____

   II. Body For each body paragraph, write a topic sentence that supports your opinion. Then list reasons, facts, and examples about the topic.

      A. Topic Sentence _____

      _____

      _____

         Detail 1: _____

         _____

         Detail 2: _____

         _____

      B. Topic Sentence _____

      _____

      _____

         Detail 1: _____

         _____

         Detail 2: _____

         _____

   III. Conclusion Restate your focus statement and make a recommendation to readers.

      In conclusion, _____

      _____

      _____

      _____

Write Your Draft

▶ **Write a draft of your opinion essay.**

Writing Prompt:
Is it humane to keep wild animals in zoos? Write an essay stating your opinion.

WORD CHOICES	
Everyday	**Precise**
catch	capture
home	habitat
happy	content, satisfied

_____
(title)

Introduction

▶ **Write your introductory statement.**

_____

_____

▶ **Write your focus statement.**

_____

_____

▶ **Type your introduction on the computer or write it on paper. Then use these linking words and phrases to complete a draft of your opinion essay.**

Body

One reason is that . . .	In addition, . . .
First of all, . . .	Another important point is . . .
One important example is . . .	Finally, . . .
A second reason is . . .	Most importantly, . . .

Conclusion

Overall, . . .	It's important that we . . .
In conclusion, . . .	On the whole, . . .

Revise Your Opinion Essay

▶ **Evaluate: Rate your essay. Then have a writing partner rate it.**

Scoring Guide			
needs improvement	average	good	excellent
1	**2**	**3**	**4**

1. **UNDERLINE** the introductory statement. Does it introduce the issue of the opinion essay?

   Self   1   2   3   4
   Partner   1   2   3   4

2. **BOX** the focus statement. Does it give the writer's opinion?

   Self   1   2   3   4
   Partner   1   2   3   4

3. **UNDERLINE** the topic sentence of each body paragraph. Do they support the focus statement?

   Self   1   2   3   4
   Partner   1   2   3   4

4. ✔**CHECK** supporting reasons and examples in each body paragraph. Are they convincing?

   Self   1   2   3   4
   Partner   1   2   3   4

5. **CIRCLE** linking words and phrases. Do they connect ideas?

   Self   1   2   3   4
   Partner   1   2   3   4

6. ★**STAR** the recommendation for readers in the conclusion.

   Self   1   2   3   4
   Partner   1   2   3   4

▶ **Discuss: Give feedback on your partner's opinion essay.**

1. Start with a positive comment about your partner's opinion essay.

   A strong part of your essay is

   _____

   _____

   The section I found most convincing is

   _____

2. Give your partner suggestions for revision.

   I have a question about _____

   _____

   This reason would be clearer if

   _____

3. Answer any questions your partner has about your suggestions.

4. Ask your partner for feedback. Use the frames below to summarize your partner's feedback.

   A strong part of my essay was . . .
   You found . . . to be most convincing.
   You had a question about . . .
   This reason would be clearer if . . .

▶ **Revise: Now revise your opinion essay.**

Grammar USING SUBJECT AND OBJECT PRONOUNS

A **pronoun** is a word that takes the place of a noun in a sentence.

- Use a **subject pronoun** in the subject of a sentence.
- Use an **object pronoun** after a verb or after a word such as *for* or *to*.

Examples	
Subject Pronoun	Object Pronoun
I have a pet turtle.	My turtle Myrtle likes **me**.
We got Myrtle at a pet adoption fair.	Myrtle crawled right up to **us**.
She eats lettuce for dinner.	Once, I gave a dead fly to **her**.

▶ Circle the correct pronoun. Write whether it is a **subject** or **object** pronoun.

1. [I Me] gave my pet rabbit to my friend.   *subject*

2. Jamal named [he him] Fangs.   _____

3. [Them They] were always together.   _____

4. It was hard for Jamal to take care of [he him].   _____

5. Jamal's mom gave [he him] to a pet store.   _____

6. Jamal and [I me] plan to visit Fangs.   _____

▶ Rewrite these sentences using a pronoun for the underlined words.

7. <u>Fangs</u> grew bigger and bigger!

_____

8. Finally, <u>Jamal and I</u> saw a family buy Fangs.

_____

_____

9. We followed <u>the family</u> out of the store.

_____

_____

10. <u>Fangs</u> looked happy when the family drove away.

_____

▶ **Edit Your Draft.** Take a close look at each sentence in your draft. **Do you use subject and object pronouns correctly?** Fix any that need correction.

Mechanics AVOIDING DOUBLE NEGATIVES

Negatives are words that mean *no* or *not*.

- Use only one negative word to express a single negative idea.
- It is incorrect to use two negatives to express a negative idea.

Examples

Correct	Incorrect
Tigers should never be pets.	Tigers shouldn't never be pets.
The alligator didn't eat anything.	The alligator didn't eat nothing.

▶ **Find and correct five errors in this paragraph.**

Student Model

CHECK AND CORRECT

☐ **UNDERLINE** one subject-object pronoun error and correct it.

☐ Correct two double-negative errors.

☐ (CIRCLE) two spelling errors and correct them.

I enjoy watching the elephants when I go to the zoo in my city. They are enormuos animals. Our zoo has a large habitatt for the elephants that provides a lot of space for them to roam. The habitat is green and grassy, and has a lot of trees. The elephants don't never seem bored. Some people say that elephants shouldn't never be kept in zoos, but me disagree. I learn a lot about elephants by watching them at the zoo!

▶ **Edit Your Draft.** Look at the sentences in your draft. **Are they free of double negatives?** Fix any double negatives.

Final Draft/Present

▶ Write a final draft of your essay on the computer or on paper. Check it again and correct any errors before you present it.

Read a Fact Sheet

A fact sheet gives technical or scientific facts about a topic. This fact sheet gives information about the American alligator.

▶ **Read the fact sheet, then answer the questions.**

American Alligator

SPECIES: *Mississippiensis*

CLASS: *Reptila (Reptile)*

DIET: *Carnivore*

LIFE SPAN: *35 to 50 years*

SIZE: *10 to 15 feet*   **WEIGHT:** *1,000 pounds*

- This species is more than 150 million years old. Alligators existed at the same time as the dinosaurs.
- American alligators in the wild live in freshwater rivers, lakes, and swamps. They can be found in the southeastern United States, primarily Florida and Louisiana.
- Although they are awkward out of water, alligators are excellent swimmers.
- Baby alligators are only 6 to 8 inches long. They are sometimes eaten by birds, raccoons, and bobcats.

National Wildlife Rescue   www.example.com/wildliferescue   1-800-555-5555

---

❶ Where do American alligators live in the wild?

Ⓐ freshwater rivers, lakes, and swamps

Ⓑ saltwater marshes and gulfs

Ⓒ zoos and animal farms

Ⓓ northern lakes

❷ Which describes baby alligators but not adults?

Ⓐ They are excellent swimmers.

Ⓑ They are awkward out of the water.

Ⓒ They are 6 to 8 inches long.

Ⓓ They are carnivores.

❸ Answer these questions to evaluate this fact sheet.

- What is the source of this fact sheet?

- Does the source seem reliable? Why or why not?

_____

_____

_____

_____

Zookeeper
Asaba Mukobi

Meet a zookeeper who takes care of the smartest animals in the zoo.

▶ **Read the interview and job information. Then answer the questions below about Asaba Mukobi's job.**

S **Scholastic: How do you take care of primates, besides feeding them?**

Asaba: Primates are very smart. They can get bored. So, we create games for them. For example, we put food at the bottom of a container so they can have fun working to get it out. We turn health checkups into games, too. The animals learn to present their ears, eyes, and mouth to the keeper for checking.

S **Do you think your job helps people and animals?**

I do. I am from Uganda, in East Africa, and I am impressed by how much people in the U.S. know about animals. People learn from visiting zoos, and that makes them more interested in protecting animals. I started a program in Uganda, so kids there learn about wild animals, too.

S **So many animals live at the zoo. How do you keep track of them?**

The zookeepers keep a log book about each animal. We keep notes about what the animal eats, and how the animal behaves. We monitor each animal's health.

1 **What kinds of records do zookeepers keep about animals?**

_____

_____

2 **How important do you think Asaba's job is? Mark the line.**

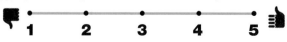

1   2   3   4   5

Not very important   **Very important**

3 **I think Asaba's job is/isn't** (circle one) **important because**

_____

_____

ON THE JOB

LOCATION

Portland, Oregon

EDUCATION

Bachelor's degree in Zoology

RESPONSIBILITIES

- Monitors animal health and well-being
- Takes careful notes
- Develops games for animals

SKILLS

- Interacting with zoo animals
- Educating people about zoo animals

SALARY

$25,000–$40,000

REWARDING PART OF THE JOB

"I have a great bond with the animals. I love working with them, and they love working with me."

CAREER CONNECTION

Education and Training
www.careerclusters.org

Related Jobs
- tour guide
- rescue shelter worker
- animal trainer

Focus Skills | Justify a Point of View | Present Effectively

Should we be allowed to have wild animals as pets?

Should people be allowed to keep wild animals as pets? Should it be illegal to have a wild pet? Hold a class debate to settle this issue.

❶ Gather information. Find facts and examples that support each side of the debate. Get information from the Workshop readings, and discuss ideas with your group.

Why Wild Pets Should Be Legal	Why Wild Pets Should Be Illegal

❷ State your opinion. Which side of the debate are you on?

It **should/should not** (circle one) *be legal to keep wild animals as pets.*

❸ Support your point of view. Brainstorm three points that express your opinion. Then list ideas, facts, and examples as evidence to support each point.

Points That Express Our Opinion	Supporting Evidence
A.	
B.	
C.	

4 **Prepare for your debate.** Organize your best ideas and practice presenting them. Before your debate, think ahead: How might the other side respond to each of your points?

> **AN EFFECTIVE DEBATE**
>
> ✓ states a clear opinion on an issue.
>
> ✓ includes examples, facts, and ideas that support the opinion.
>
> ✓ responds to the other side's opinions.

DEBATE: Should people be allowed to keep wild animals as pets?

OPENING STATEMENT: _____
_____
_____
_____
_____

OUR SIDE:

A. _____
_____
_____
_____

B. _____
_____
_____
_____

C. _____
_____
_____
_____

POSSIBLE RESPONSE:

A. _____
_____
_____
_____

B. _____
_____
_____
_____

C. _____
_____
_____
_____

SUMMARY/CLOSING STATEMENT: In conclusion, people **should/should not** (circle one) be allowed to keep wild animals as pets because _____
_____
_____

Comprehension

▶ **Choose the best answer to each question. Fill in the bubble.**

1. Ming the tiger was taken away from Antoine Yates because Ming _____.

Ⓐ ate a neighbor's dog

Ⓑ bit Yates

Ⓒ bit a veterinarian

Ⓓ was growling all night

> **Here's a Tip.**
> Look for words like *why*, *cause*, *effect*, *problem*, *solution*, and *because* in the questions. These cue words help you figure out what kind of answer is expected.

2. Why do so many wild animal pets end up abandoned at shelters?

Ⓐ They are too boring for owners to enjoy them.

Ⓑ They escape from owners' homes and are caught by police.

Ⓒ They need expensive food and can become dangerous.

Ⓓ Owners feel sorry for them and want them to go back to the wild.

3. Why do some people think that wild pets should be outlawed?

Ⓐ They are too big.

Ⓑ They are too dangerous.

Ⓒ They are too pretty.

Ⓓ They are too unhappy.

4. Analyze: Experts believe that snow leopards in zoos are less bored than many other large zoo animals. Why?

Ⓐ Snow leopards prefer to see humans than to see other leopards.

Ⓑ Snow leopards do not have a big need to roam, even in the wild.

Ⓒ Polar bears and snow leopards hunt each other in some zoos.

Ⓓ Snow leopards perform tricks in shows at some zoos.

CRITICAL READING

5. Evaluate: According to the Workshop, how are many zoos improving?

Ⓐ They are making zoo animals do fewer tricks.

Ⓑ They are adding more animals to each cage so that no zoo animals become lonely.

Ⓒ They are making animals' exhibits more like the animals' homes in the wild.

Ⓓ They are closing many exhibits that people no longer find interesting.

CRITICAL READING

Vocabulary

▶ **Choose the answer that best defines the underlined word.**

1. Wild pets can be a <u>threat</u> to their owners.
   Ⓐ friend
   Ⓑ punishment
   Ⓒ joy
   Ⓓ danger

2. In their home <u>habitat</u>, polar bears are used to roaming long distances.
   Ⓐ family group
   Ⓑ natural environment
   Ⓒ zoo cages
   Ⓓ state

3. <u>Enormous</u> elephants seem peaceful, but when attacked, they can be <u>fierce</u>.
   Ⓐ very large; wild and violent
   Ⓑ young; unhappy
   Ⓒ big-eared; loud
   Ⓓ pretty; ugly

▶ **Mark the correct form of *capture* in the following sentence.**

4. The police _____ the bear that attacked the campers.
   Ⓐ capture
   Ⓑ capturing
   Ⓒ captured
   Ⓓ capturer

▶ **Choose the correct definition for *range* as it is used in this sentence.**

5. The ice cream store offers a <u>range</u> of flavors.
   Ⓐ area where an animal roams
   Ⓑ a variety
   Ⓒ least amount
   Ⓓ a line of mountains

Short Answer

CRITICAL READING

▶ **Synthesize: Use what you've read in this Workshop to answer the question. Check your spelling and grammar.**

Would you vote for or against legalizing wild pets in your town? Explain.

_____

_____

_____

WORKSHOP 8

INFORMATIONAL TEXT

COMPREHENSION FOCUS
Compare and Contrast

CRITICAL READING FOCUS
Analyze
Synthesize
Evaluate

Reading 1 Food Fight: Chefs vs. Kids |
News Article

Reading 2 Bugs vs. Burgers | **Magazine Article**

Reading 3 You Are What You Eat |
Health Science Feature

FOOD: The Good, the Bad, and the GROSS

Some foods are good for us. Some foods are bad for us. And some foods are just plain gross! Get ready to take a food tour that includes all three.

You'll sample school cafeteria menus, compare the tastes of bugs and burgers, and finish up with tips for a healthy diet and exercise. Hold on to your stomach, and get ready to read!

Academic Vocabulary

Target Word	Meaning	Examples
▶ Read the Target Words. Rate each one using the scale below.*	▶ Read the Target Word meanings. Write in the missing words.	▶ Finish the Target Word examples below. Write in the missing ones.
nutritious (p. 212) _nu•tri•tious_ (adjective) ① ② ③ ④	healthy to eat	• _____ _____ would be a **nutritious** breakfast. • _____ _____
prefer (p. 212) _pre•fer_ (verb) ① ② ③ ④	to _____ one thing _____ than another	• I **prefer** _____ to _____ • _____ _____
appealing (p. 212) _ap•peal•ing_ (adjective) ① ② ③ ④	to seem _____ or interesting	• Foods that are **appealing** to me are _____ • _____ _____
satisfy (p. 212) _sat•is•fy_ (verb) ① ② ③ ④	to please by giving what someone wants or needs	• I **satisfied** my parents by _____ • _____ _____
variety (p. 216) _va•ri•e•ty_ (noun) ① ② ③ ④	1. a selection of _____ 2. a type of something that is different from others in its group	Apples come in a **variety** of colors.

*Rating Scale ① = I don't know the word. ③ = I think I know the word. ② = I've seen it or heard it. ④ = I know it and use it.

Food: The Good, the Bad, and the Gross **211**

The Key Idea

▶ **WRITE** What is this article mostly about?

_____

_____

_____

VOCABULARY
 Target Word

habit

hab•it (noun)

Rate It: ① ② ③ ④

Meaning

an activity you do _____ _____ without thinking

Example

A good study **habit** is _____

_____

⊘ **React and Write**

▶ **WRITE** How would you rate your school's lunches? What would make your school's lunches better?

💬 **Summarize**

In one or two sentences, summarize how chefs try to make lunches healthier. Include the topic and important details.

FOOD FIGHT: Chefs vs. Kids
School Chefs and Students Face Off

Kids check out what's for lunch.

by Owen Hayes

September 7—There's a new lunch menu in New York City schools. New chefs want to offer healthier options. But they are off to a rough start. Many students have a **habit** of eating only junk food.

So, what's for lunch? Both chefs and kids love burgers. Chefs serve up nutritious veggie burgers. But students don't bite. They want meat burgers. The veggie burgers have a "weird flavor," one student says.

Chefs know that side dishes can make or break a meal. Kids think so, too. So, chefs offer baked fries and vegetables. However, students prefer _fried_ fries. One student thinks vegetables are not very appealing. "They don't taste good," she says.

Chefs like to provide dessert. Kids also want dessert. That's why chefs offer fruit. Does that work? No! Instead of trying a pear, students select cookies from vending machines.

Chefs keep trying. But nothing is working! How can they satisfy students and make food healthier? The girl who hates veggies has an idea. "You have to hide the vegetables where I can't see them," she says. ⟨END⟩

Words to Know! **select** to choose

Comprehension Focus

Compare and Contrast

When you **compare**, you tell how two things are the same. When you **contrast**, you tell how they are different. To compare and contrast:

- Ask yourself how two things are the same. Look for signal words such as *both*, *too*, *also*, and *in addition*.

- Ask yourself how two things are different. Look for signal words such as *but*, *rather than*, *however*, *unlike*, and *instead*.

▶ Complete this chart to compare and contrast what the school chefs want to serve and what the students want to eat.

School Chefs

Different

1. **Burgers**

_____

_____

2. **Side Dishes**

_____

_____

3. **Desserts**

_____

_____

Same

1. **Burgers**

Both groups think burgers are a good main course.

2. **Side Dishes**

Both groups want side dishes to be part of lunch.

3. **Desserts**

Both groups know that students love dessert.

Students

Different

1. **Burgers**

_____

_____

2. **Side Dishes**

_____

_____

3. **Desserts**

_____

_____

This Thai woman is selling roasted grasshoppers in a market.

Bugs vs. Burgers

by Daniel Kim

Are bugs totally gross to eat? Read the facts— you may change your mind!

The World Loves Bugs

Most people think bugs are just delicious. In fact, 80 percent of people around the world eat bugs. Some families in Venezuela roast tarantulas over fires. In South Africa, many people go buggy over fried termites. In Japan, diners may spend as much as $40 on one plate of baby stone flies!

Most Americans, however, think bugs are gross. The only Americans you might see eating bugs are those trying to win a million dollars on TV. The **average** American would much rather eat a juicy burger than a juicy bug!

Are bugs *really* disgusting? Your answer probably depends on what you're used to eating. That's how most people decide what's good and what's gross. But there's more to the story. How nutritious are bugs, compared with burgers? How hard is it to grow and cook bugs? And do burgers really win the taste test?

Here's to Your Health

Doctors say that a diet high in protein and low in fat is a good way to improve your health. It can prevent heart disease or diabetes.

The average beef burger is packed with protein! A burger with all the fixings has about 25 grams of protein. Burgers also have about 27 grams of fat.

How do bugs compare? Like burgers, bugs are packed with protein. A dinner of grasshoppers has about 21 grams of protein. Unlike burgers, bugs have very little fat. That dinner of grasshoppers has only 6 grams of fat. For a nutritious meal, bugs win out over beef burgers. ➤

Words to Know! **percent** part of a whole

Compare and Contrast

1. ▷ **WRITE** How are Americans different from 80 percent of the world?

_____

_____

_____

_____

2. <u>UNDERLINE</u> Find one similarity between bugs and burgers.

3. (CIRCLE) Identify one difference between bugs and burgers.

CRITICAL READING
Evaluate

▷ **WRITE** Why are bugs more nutritious than burgers?

_____

_____

_____

_____

Active Reading

★**STAR** What do some bugs taste like?

 VOCABULARY
Target Word

adjust

ad•just (verb)

Rate It: ① ② ③ ④

Meaning

to move or _____

something _____

Example

Restaurants could **adjust** their

menus by _____

_____

_____

_____

 React and Write

▶ **WRITE** If a friend served you a bug sandwich, would you try it? Why or why not?

 Summarize

In one or two sentences, summarize the topic and important details in "Fast Food."

Fast Food

There are also big differences between how we get bugs and beef. Bugs and cows can both be raised on farms. Crickets are raised in just six weeks. Farmers need only 100 pounds of feed to raise 45 pounds of crickets. However, cows take two years to raise. To get 45 pounds of beef, farmers must use a whopping 1,125 pounds of feed. That's ten times as much feed as crickets need.

Fried grasshoppers can be a yummy treat!

Burger restaurants are much easier for Americans to find than bug stands. Many fast food restaurants sell burgers. But bugs can be found only in specialty stores and restaurants and online.

At home, both bugs and burgers are easy to cook. Burgers are usually fried up in a pan. Bugs can be made this way, too. Just add salt and ketchup and enjoy! But watch out: Some bugs are poisonous!

The Taste Test

Burgers taste meaty and salty—flavors that appeal to most Americans. Bug-eaters say bugs are yummy, too. Unlike burgers, bugs come in a variety of complex flavors. A type of Mexican stinkbug has a cinnamon flavor. Most bugs are crunchy on the outside—like popcorn!

Bugs are nutritious, cheap, and yummy. Will Americans **adjust** their tastes and learn to love them? We'll have to wait and see.

So, the next time you suffer from a bug bite, remember—it might be time to bite back! END

Words to Know! | **complex** with many parts

Comprehension Focus

Compare and Contrast

▶ Complete this chart to compare and contrast bugs and burgers, using information from the sections "Fast Food" and "The Taste Test."

Bugs

Different

1. _____

_____

_____

2. _____

_____

_____

3. _____

_____

_____

Same

1. _____

_____

_____

2. _____

_____

_____

3. _____

_____

Burgers

Different

1. _____

_____

_____

2. _____

_____

_____

3. _____

_____

_____

The Key Idea

▶ **WRITE** What is this article mostly about?

_____

_____

VOCABULARY
Target Word

neglect

ne•glect (verb)

Rate It: ① ② ③ ④

Meaning

_____ to take care

of someone or something

Example

By _____

_____

Zac **neglected** his health.

React and Write

▶ **WRITE** Which of the activities on page 219 would you most want to do? Explain why.

You Are What You EAT

by Aasha Gibson

Zac Garcia prepares a salad at home.

Kids today aren't very healthy. It's time to do something–before it's too late.

Getting Healthy

Sixth grader Zac Garcia wasn't feeling so good. On an average day, he was tired. He didn't have much energy. So, he decided to improve his health. First, he adjusted his diet. He ate larger portions of fruits and vegetables. He also ate nutritious snacks.

Then, Zac adjusted his exercise habits. He had always been active. But he wanted to do even more. He started riding his bike more often. He started walking more.

Within six months, Zac had lost 10 pounds. These days, he has less fat and more muscle. He also has more energy. "I used to run a mile in 10.5 minutes. Now I run a mile in only 9.5," he said.

Get Physical

Many kids **neglect** to exercise enough. The average kid spends less than 15 minutes a day working out. Being active can be a challenge. But it can also be fun. Zac chose biking and walking. There are a variety of ways to get exercise. Any of these activities will burn 150 calories:

- Wash and wax a car for 45–60 minutes
- Rake leaves for 30 minutes
- Walk two miles in 30 minutes
- Play touch football for 45 minutes
- Wheel self in a wheelchair for 30–40 minutes
- In-line skate for 20–25 minutes ➤

Words to Know!	**portion**	an amount of food for one person

📖 Compare and Contrast

1. CIRCLE Identify the paragraph that contrasts Zac's weight and energy level before and after he changed his habits.

2. ▶ WRITE Which listed activity burns 150 calories most slowly?

_____

_____

3. ▶ WRITE Which activity burns 150 calories most quickly?

_____

_____

📖 REVIEW Cause and Effect

▶ WRITE What effect did Zac's new habits have on his running?

_____

_____

_____

🧠 CRITICAL READING Synthesize

▶ WRITE What could you do to improve your health? Use facts from the reading in your response.

_____

_____

Active Reading

★**STAR** What diseases can people get from a high-fat diet?

 Target Word

necessity

ne•ces•si•ty *(noun)*

Rate It: ① ② ③ ④

Meaning

a strong _____

or requirement

Example

_____

_____ is a **necessity**

for doing well in school.

 React and Write

▶ **WRITE** What is your favorite snack? Is it healthy?

 Summarize

▶ **WRITE** Summarize the topic and important details in the health science feature "You Are What You Eat."

Burgers and Fries

Not every kid is as healthy as Zac. In fact, in 2008, nearly one in three U.S. children were overweight, and 16 percent were obese. That's more kids than ever before. Back in 1980, for example, only 5.7 percent of children were overweight.

What's going on? Experts say many American kids prefer fast food to healthier options. It's a favorite source for food. Americans spend $110 billion on fast food. That's more than they spend on movies, books, magazines, videos, and music—combined! The average American eats three burgers and four orders of french fries per week.

The Science Behind the Diet

What's wrong with a fast food diet? It may satisfy your taste buds. However, it's not so great for your health. Most fast food comes from two food groups: meat and fat. The Food Guide Pyramid below shows how much to eat from each group.

Words to Know! **source** where something comes from

TEXT FEATURE Reading a Diagram

The Food Guide Pyramid

The widest triangles show the foods we need most and the narrowest triangles show foods we need the least. Grains should be a big part of every diet. Fruits and vegetables should also be eaten often. Fats and meats are a **necessity**, too. But we should eat them only in small amounts.

When people eat too much fat, their bodies suffer. Fats, oils, and sweets in your diet can lead to weight gain. That can lead to diabetes, heart disease, and even arthritis.

If you want to be healthy, check out the Food Guide Pyramid. How do your eating habits compare? Then, ask your doctor about a good diet for you. Get started with good eating habits—and you'll probably keep them for life. END

A diagram is a drawing that explains something.

❶ From which food group should you select the *most* servings daily?

Ⓐ fruits　　Ⓑ oil　　Ⓒ grains　　Ⓓ milk

❷ Aside from oils, which food group should you eat the *least* of each day?

Ⓐ meat and beans　Ⓑ milk　Ⓒ fruits　Ⓓ grains

❸ **Synthesize:** Looking at the chart, are there any groups from which you don't eat enough servings? Explain.

_____

_____

Compare and Contrast

1. CIRCLE Identify the paragraph that contrasts children in 1980 with children in 2008.

2. UNDERLINE How much do Americans spend on fast food, compared with other items?

CRITICAL READING
Analyze

▶ **WRITE** According to the reading, what can people do to help prevent diabetes and heart disease?

_____

_____

_____

_____

Skills Check

1. ✔ CHECK From which two food groups does most fast food come?

2. ▶ WRITE How much oil and meat should people eat, contrasted with grains, vegetables, and fruits?

_____

_____

_____

Word Challenge

start

It's so cold outside, I'd better **adjust** my outfit. I'll **change** into a sweater.

1
Rate them. Which activity **appeals** to you most? Which **appeals** to you least?

1 = most **appealing**
4 = least **appealing**

____ riding a roller coaster

____ eating a worm

____ dyeing your hair green

____ giving a class report

2 Synonyms

Synonyms are words that have similar meanings. Examples are *smart* and *clever*, or *boring* and *dull*.

Match each word below to its synonym.

illness   fun

similar   giant

enjoyable   sickness

huge   alike

3
Ask yourself. Which of these do you sometimes **neglect**? Write **N** next to anything that you sometimes **neglect**.

____ your friends   ____ your pet

____ your chores   ____ your family

____ your homework   ____ exercising

4
Choose them. In each row, circle the item that you **prefer**.

cats   **OR**   dogs

football   **OR**   baseball

TV   **OR**   movies

drawing   **OR**   reading

5
Evaluate. Which might you say if you were *very* **satisfied** with something?

☐ "Well, it's OK . . . I guess."

☐ "Great! Perfect! I love it!"

☐ "This could be better."

6

Identify them. Which of these foods do you think are **nutritious**? Check them. Then circle the foods you most enjoy eating.

- ☐ grasshoppers
- ☐ fish soup
- ☐ vegetable soup
- ☐ potato chips
- ☐ jelly beans
- ☐ fruit salad
- ☐ ice cream
- ☐ hamburgers
- ☐ veggie burgers

7 Suffixes

> My dog may not be **powerful**, but he is very **lovable**.

A **suffix** is a letter or group of letters added to the end of a word. A suffix changes the meaning or part of speech of a word. The suffix *-able* changes a verb to an adjective. The suffix *-ful* changes a noun or verb to an adjective.

Fill in. Change these verbs to adjectives by adding the suffix *-able* or *-ful*.

adjust _____

neglect _____

believe _____

wonder _____

8

Consider it. Name three activities you might do on an **average** school night.

1. _____
   _____

2. _____
   _____

3. _____
   _____

9

Analyze. Name three things you think are **necessities** for having a good party.

- _____
- _____
- _____

10

Finish them. Complete the first sentence by writing **habits** or **variety** in the correct blanks. Complete the second sentence with your own idea.

My little brother has a _____ of bad _____, like tapping his fingers and chewing smelly bubble gum. But the worst thing he does is _____.

finish

Writing Text Type
Research Paper

A **research paper** presents information on a subject. The information is gathered from several reliable sources.

▶ **Read student Ashley Bennett's research paper about the effects of bullying.**

Student Model

Introduction

An **introductory statement** introduces the topic.

1. **UNDERLINE** the **introductory statement**.

The introductory paragraph includes a clear **focus statement** that gives a plan for the paper.

2. **BOX** the **focus statement**.

Body

Each body paragraph starts with a **topic sentence** that includes a **controlling idea**.

3. **BOX** the **controlling idea** in each topic sentence.

Facts and examples support each topic sentence.

4. **✔CHECK** four supporting **facts and examples**.

Multiple sources of information are **cited**.

5. **CIRCLE** four **citations**.

Conclusion

The **conclusion** sums up the ideas about the topic.

6. **★STAR** the **conclusion**.

Bullying: A Serious Problem
by Ashley Bennett

Bullying is a major problem in many schools. Bullying is widespread and can have long-lasting negative effects on victims.

More than half of all kids ages 8–11 worry about bullies (DeSilva 100). Some victims can't focus on schoolwork. Others skip school to avoid bullies. Some victims feel so upset that they may become bullies themselves (Wilson, Johnson, Diego 92).

The effects of bullying can last a long time. A girl named Keesha was bothered by bullies who called her names and threw food at her (Bromley 94, 96). The bullies were suspended, but Keesha still feels troubled when she thinks about them. Another victim says she is always nervous in school, even though her bully was moved to a different class (Bromley 96).

In conclusion, bullying is a serious problem for grade-school students. Victims of bullying suffer when they are bullied. In fact, many still feel the pain long after the bullying stops.

B I U

P 1

Analyze the Text Type

▶ **Work with a partner to understand the purpose and form of a research paper.**

Purpose: Research Paper
The purpose of a research paper is to _____ _____

Introduction

The **introductory paragraph** of a research paper:

1. introduces _____

2. includes _____ that gives a _____

| **Student Model** | In her introduction, Ashley Bennett: |

1. introduces the topic of _____

2. includes a clear focus statement, which is: _____
_____

Body

1. Each **body** paragraph starts with a _____

2. _____ support the writer's topic sentences.

| **Student Model** |

1. The topic sentence for Ashley Bennett's first body paragraph is _____
_____

2. Two facts or examples in the first body paragraph are:

• _____
• _____

Conclusion

The **conclusion** sums up _____

| **Student Model** | Ashley Bennett concludes her research paper by stating _____
_____
_____

Prewrite

Writing Topic:

Write a research paper about the importance of a healthy diet.

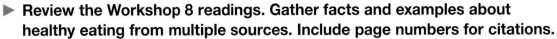

▶ **Review the Workshop 8 readings. Gather facts and examples about healthy eating from multiple sources. Include page numbers for citations.**

Source 1: _____

Source 2: _____

Source 3: _____

State Your Topic

▶ **Use your notes to help you state the topic.**

I plan to write about _____

I will use evidence to argue that _____

_____

Organize Ideas for Writing

▶ **Complete this outline with notes for your research paper.**

I. Introduction State your topic and your focus statement.

Topic: _____

Focus Statement: _____

_____

II. Body Write a topic sentence for each body paragraph that supports your focus statement. Then list facts and examples that support each topic sentence. Include the author's last name and page numbers for citations.

A. Topic Sentence _____

_____

Facts/Examples: _____

_____

Facts/Examples: _____

_____

B. Topic Sentence _____

_____

Facts/Examples: _____

_____

Facts/Examples: _____

_____

III. Conclusion Sum up your ideas about the topic.

In conclusion, _____

_____

_____

_____

_____

_____

_____

Write Your Draft

▶ **Write a draft of your research paper.**

Writing Prompt:

Write a research paper about the importance of eating a healthy diet. Support your ideas with evidence from the Workshop readings.

WORD CHOICES	
Everyday	**Precise**
choose	select
help	benefit
size	portion

_____
(title)

Introduction

▶ **Write your introductory statement.**

It is important to eat healthy food because _____
(topic)

_____

▶ **Write your focus statement.**

Eating a healthy diet helps you by _____
(effects)

_____

▶ **Type your introduction on the computer or write it on paper. Then use these linking words and phrases to complete a draft of your research paper.**

Body

First of all, . . .	*Another important point is . . .*
For example, . . .	*According to . . .*
Another reason . . .	*Finally, . . .*
In addition . . .	*Most important, . . .*

Conclusion

In conclusion, . . .	*It is clear that . . .*
In summary, . . .	*Based on my research, . . .*

Revise Your Research Paper

▶ **Evaluate: Rate your paper. Then have a writing partner rate it.**

Scoring Guide			
needs improvement	average	good	excellent
1	**2**	**3**	**4**

1. **UNDERLINE** the introductory statement. Does it introduce the topic effectively?

   Self   1   2   3   4
   Partner   1   2   3   4

2. **BOX** the focus statement. Does it give a clear plan for the paper?

   Self   1   2   3   4
   Partner   1   2   3   4

3. **BOX** the topic sentences. Do they include controlling ideas?

   Self   1   2   3   4
   Partner   1   2   3   4

4. ✔**CHECK** facts and examples in the body paragraphs. Do they support each topic sentence?

   Self   1   2   3   4
   Partner   1   2   3   4

5. **CIRCLE** the citations. Are they from several different sources?

   Self   1   2   3   4
   Partner   1   2   3   4

6. ★**STAR** the conclusion. Does it sum up the writer's ideas about the topic?

   Self   1   2   3   4
   Partner   1   2   3   4

▶ **Discuss: Give feedback on your partner's research paper.**

1. Start with a positive comment about your partner's research paper.

   A strong part of your research paper is

   _____

   I enjoyed reading the section about

   _____

2. Give your partner suggestions for revision.

   I have a question about _____

   _____

   Your paper would be clearer if you

   _____

   Your research paper needs to include

   _____

3. Answer any questions your partner has about your suggestions.

4. Use the frames below to summarize your partner's feedback.

   A strong part of my paper was . . .
   You had a question about . . .
   My paper would be clearer if I . . .
   My research paper needs . . .
   You enjoyed the section about . . .

▶ **Revise: Now revise your research paper.**

Grammar USING ADJECTIVES THAT COMPARE

An **adjective** is a word that tells about, or describes, a noun. Adjectives can help compare two or more people, places, or things.

- To use an adjective to **compare two things**, add *-er* to the adjective or use the word *more*.
- To use an adjective to **compare three or more things**, add *-est* to the adjective or use the word *most*.

Examples

Adjective Comparing Two Things	Adjective Comparing Three or More Things
Zac is **stronger** than his friend.	He is the **strongest** kid in his class.
Zac is **more athletic** than his friend.	He is the **most athletic** student in his class.

▶ **Circle the correct adjective in the sentences below.**

1. Your burger is [greasier greasiest] than this veggie burger.
2. That was the [grosser grossest] meal I've ever eaten.
3. This salad is the [more most] healthy meal you could eat.
4. Americans eat [larger largest] portions than the Japanese.
5. Meat should be the [smaller smallest] portion on our plate.
6. I think pizza is probably [more most] tasty than bugs.

▶ **Rewrite the sentences to compare three or more things correctly.**

7. Zac is the <u>more</u> active person in his family.

_____

8. Zac now runs the <u>faster</u> mile of all his classmates.

_____

9. Who gets the <u>more</u> exercise in your class?

_____

10. Americans should try to be the <u>healthier</u> people in the world.

_____

▶ **Edit Your Draft.** Take a close look at each of the sentences in your draft. **Do they use adjectives that compare correctly?** Fix any that don't.

Usage CORRECTING SENTENCE FRAGMENTS

Each sentence must state a complete idea.

- You can often add a subject or a verb to a sentence fragment to form a complete sentence.

Examples

Correct	Incorrect
Zac changed his diet.	Changed his diet. [missing subject]
He started walking more.	He walking more. [missing verb]

▶ **Find and correct five errors in this paragraph.**

Student Model

Eating an unhealthy diet is a problem. Among school children. Most children perfer to eat junk food (Hayes 212). Junk food has a lot of fat and can cause weight gain. In fact, in 2008, almost 1 in 3 children were overweight (Gibson 220). Most children need to ajust their diets and eat smallest portions of food. A good way to stay healthy. Exercise a lot, and eat a diet mostly of grains, vegetables, and fruits.

CHECK AND CORRECT

- ☐ **UNDERLINE** two sentence fragments.
- ☐ Correct one error with a comparison.
- ☐ CIRCLE two spelling errors and correct them.

▶ **Edit Your Draft.** Look at the sentences in your draft. **Does each sentence contain a subject and verb?** Fix any that do not.

Final Draft/Present

▶ **Write a final draft of your paper on the computer or on paper. Check it again and correct any errors before you present it.**

Focus Skill | Set Goals

Read a Menu

Use this menu to help you choose healthy lunch foods.

▶ **Read the menu. Then answer the questions.**

MARK IT

- **UNDERLINE** two items made with fresh fruit.
- **CIRCLE** the calorie count for each item.
- ★**STAR** the fat content of each item.

Frida's Family Foods

LUNCH MENU

MAIN COURSES

	CALORIES	FAT	PRICE
HOT DOG	320	19.5G	$3.00
HAMBURGER	645	37G	$3.25
FISH SANDWICH	235	23G	$2.75
NACHOS	223	22G	$7.00
HUMMUS & VEGGIE PLATE	108	5G	$6.00

DRINKS

	CALORIES	FAT	PRICE
MILKSHAKE	760	28G	$4.50
FRESH-SQUEEZED ORANGE JUICE	100	.3G	$5.00
SODA	100	0G	$2.00
WATER	0	0G	$1.50

DESSERT

	CALORIES	FAT	PRICE
FRESH FRUIT CUP	74	.2G	$5.00
COOKIES	138	8G	$2.00
ICE CREAM	260	16G	$3.50

 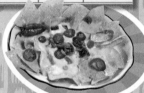

① **Which main course item has the most calories and the most fat?**

Ⓐ nachos

Ⓒ fish sandwich

Ⓑ hot dog

Ⓓ hamburger

② **Which statement is true?**

Ⓐ Items are priced according to how healthy they are.

Ⓑ A fish sandwich costs more than a hamburger.

Ⓒ One of the drinks has more calories than each of the main course foods.

Ⓓ The most expensive menu item has the most calories and fat.

③ **Which food, dessert, and drink could you choose for a low-fat, healthy lunch? Explain.**

_____

_____

_____

_____

_____

_____

Restaurant Manager
Tiffanie Masutani

Meet a restaurant manager who makes sure dining out is a memorable experience for her customers.

▶ **Read the daily log and job information. Then answer the questions below about Tiffanie Masutani's job.**

3 P.M. At the start of my shift, I visit diners at their tables to make sure they are happy with their meals. I check with the waiters to see if they need anything. We all sing "Happy Birthday" to a boy who is turning 10 years old.

6 P.M. The dinner rush starts. A line of people waits to be seated. The rush usually lasts until around 9 P.M.

8 P.M. I see some regulars, a couple who comes every Friday night. I ask how their week was. I make sure they can sit down while waiting. Regulars are our best customers!

11 P.M. Closing time! As we wait for the last guests to leave, the dining room staff refills salt and pepper shakers. When the room empties, we turn up the lights and get the room ready for tomorrow's breakfast shift. We vacuum rugs, wipe down tables and chairs, and go home with tired feet.

❶ Tiffanie's goal is to make sure customers are satisfied. How does she do this? Identify two ways.

_____

_____

❷ How stressful do you think Tiffanie's job is? Mark the line.

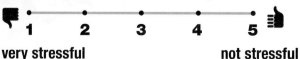

1 2 3 4 5
very stressful   **not stressful**

❸ I think Tiffanie's job is/isn't (circle one) stressful because

_____

ON THE JOB

LOCATION
Aiea, Hawaii

EDUCATION
Bachelor's degree in Culinary Management

RESPONSIBILITIES
- Helps waiters
- Checks in with customers
- Monitors waitstaff schedule

SKILLS
- Making conversation
- Staying calm
- Solving problems

SALARY
Experienced restaurant managers make between $30,000 and $45,000.

REWARDING PART OF THE JOB
"It's great to meet and get to know families who make us one of their traditions."

CAREER CONNECTION

Hospitality and Tourism
www.careerclusters.org

Related Jobs
- waiter
- chef
- caterer

Are your school's lunches healthy?

Can students at your school choose fresh fruits and vegetables? Low-fat milk instead of soda? Write an email to propose three changes that would make lunches healthier at your school.

❶ Gather information. Think about the Workshop readings and your own experience. List tips for healthy eating.

A. _____

B. _____

C. _____

D. _____

❷ Build a team. Assign roles for a Healthy Lunch Team. Describe how each team member will help make school lunches more nutritious.

1. Our school chef/menu planner _____
   (name)

   will _____

2. Nutrition experts _____ and _____
   (name)   (name)

   will _____

3. Student representatives _____ and _____
   (name)   (name)

   will _____

❸ Collaborate. As the Healthy Lunch Team, brainstorm ways to make school lunches healthier—and still delicious. Discuss the pros and cons of all the ideas. Then circle the three best ideas for your school.

- _____

- _____

- _____

- _____

④ **Write an email.** Write an email to your principal. Suggest three changes to make school lunches healthier. Explain why you made these suggestions.

Email

☉ **Send**   ☒ **Delete**   ✎ **Attachment**

FROM: The Healthy Lunch Team

TO: Our School Principal

SUBJECT: Healthier school lunches

Dear Principal _____ :
                              (name)

As the Healthy Lunch Team, we propose these three healthy changes:

1. _____

_____

2. _____

_____

3. _____

_____

These changes will make school lunches healthier because _____

_____

_____

We hope you will put this plan into action, so that students at our school will be healthier. Thank you for your time.

Sincerely,

The Healthy Lunch Team

Comprehension

▶ **Fill in the bubble next to the correct answer.**

1. Which healthy foods do school chefs try to serve to kids?

Ⓐ cinnamon rolls

Ⓑ burgers and cookies

Ⓒ fruits and vegetables

Ⓓ bugs

> **Here's a Tip.**
> Read over your answers carefully. Double-check that you filled in the correct circle for each answer you chose.

2. Evaluate: How do bugs and burgers compare in terms of health benefits?

CRITICAL READING

Ⓐ Bugs are healthier because they have less fat than burgers.

Ⓑ Bugs are healthier because they are crunchier than burgers.

Ⓒ Burgers are healthier because they come from cows.

Ⓓ Bugs and burgers have the exact same health benefits.

3. How many people around the world eat bugs?

Ⓐ only a few—about 10 percent

Ⓑ about half—about 50 percent

Ⓒ most—about 80 percent

Ⓓ All people around the world eat bugs.

4. Analyze: Which is NOT an effective form of exercise?

CRITICAL READING

Ⓐ walking to school

Ⓑ playing sports

Ⓒ playing video games

Ⓓ riding a bike

5. What is one way to eat more healthily?

Ⓐ Eat daily recommended amounts from each food group.

Ⓑ Eat foods that have been recommended by popular students.

Ⓒ Eat fresh fruits and vegetables and nothing else for as long as you can.

Ⓓ Choose snacks according to what tastes best to you.

Vocabulary

▶ **Fill in the circle next to the correct definitions of the underlined words.**

1. We have to run a mile in under ten minutes to <u>satisfy</u> our coach.
- Ⓐ to please someone
- Ⓑ to make someone angry
- Ⓒ to make someone sleepy
- Ⓓ to make someone sad

2. Books about sports <u>appeal</u> to me more than books about science.
- Ⓐ to disgust
- Ⓑ to challenge
- Ⓒ to seem likable
- Ⓓ to be longer

3. My family eats a <u>variety</u> of foods, but burritos are our favorite.
- Ⓐ food from Mexico
- Ⓑ selection of different things
- Ⓒ color
- Ⓓ large amount

▶ **Choose the best word to fill in the blank.**

4. I think chocolate ice cream is _____ to vanilla.
- Ⓐ prefer
- Ⓑ preferring
- Ⓒ preferable
- Ⓓ preferless

▶ **Choose the synonym for the underlined word.**

5. Vegetables are part of a <u>nutritious</u> diet.
- Ⓐ unhealthy
- Ⓑ boring
- Ⓒ exciting
- Ⓓ healthy

Short Answer

CRITICAL READING

▶ **Synthesize: Use what you've read in this Workshop to answer the question below. Check your spelling and grammar.**

Describe what you ate for breakfast today. Was it healthy? Was it delicious?

_____

_____

_____

COMPREHENSION FOCUS
Make Inferences

CRITICAL READING FOCUS
Analyze
Synthesize
Evaluate

No Small Hero

In 1960, Ruby Bridges was a first grader. On the day she started school, Ruby made history. She was the first— and only—African-American student to go to her school.

Ruby became a hero of the Civil Rights Movement. She was brave. She was strong. She was just six years old.

Academic Vocabulary

◎ Target Word	Meaning	Examples
▶ Read the Target Words. Rate each one using the scale below.*	▶ Read the Target Word meanings. Write in the missing words.	▶ Finish the Target Word examples below. Write in the missing ones.
serious (p. 243) se•ri•ous (adjective) ① ② ③ ④	_____ and solemn	Jakob is in a **serious** mood today.
frightened (p. 243) fright•ened (adjective) ① ② ③ ④	afraid	• I am **frightened** of _____ _____ • _____ _____
influence (p. 249) in•flu•ence (verb) ① ② ③ ④	to have _____ on someone or _____	• Our friends often **influence** _____ _____ • _____ _____
admire (p. 249) ad•mire (verb) ① ② ③ ④	to _____ and _____ someone	• _____ is one person I **admire**. • _____ _____
opportunity (p. 249) op•por•tu•ni•ty (noun) ① ② ③ ④	a chance to do something	• Going to a new school is an **opportunity** to _____ • _____ _____

Rating Scale
① = I don't know the word. **③** = I think I know the word.
② = I've seen it or heard it. **④** = I know it and use it.

No Small Hero 239

The Key Idea

▶**WRITE** What is this nonfiction article mostly about?

_____

_____

_____

VOCABULARY
Target Word

ignore

ig•nore (verb)

Rate It: ① ② ③ ④

Meaning

to take _____

of _____

Example

I **ignore** everything around me

when _____

React and Write

▶**WRITE** If you were Ruby, would you have wanted to go to William Frantz Public School? Why or why not?

Summarize

In one or two sentences, summarize the hardships Ruby and her family endured to get her a better education. Include the topic and important details.

Ruby Bridges

One little girl fought for equal rights

Ruby Bridges became a hero at the age of six. In 1954, the United States Supreme Court had made a decision. They ruled that it was unfair for African-American children and white children to go to separate schools. But for many years after that, states in the South **ignored** the order for schools to integrate.

Louisiana was one of those states. New Orleans, the city where Ruby's family lived, was given a deadline. They had to start integrating schools by September 1960. That was the year that Ruby would be a first grader.

At the end of kindergarten, African-American kindergartners were given a test. Children who passed would be allowed to go to the white schools. The test was hard. But Ruby did well. She was chosen to attend William Frantz Public School. Three other children would attend a different school.

Ruby would get a better education at the new school. But it came at a great cost. Many people were angry. They threatened Ruby. White parents wouldn't let their children be in her class. Her principal treated her unfairly. And her father was fired from his job.

But Ruby proved that one small person can make a big difference. ⟨END⟩

Words to Know! **integrate** to include people of all races

Comprehension Focus

Make Inferences

When you **make inferences**, you form ideas about things that are not directly stated in the text. To make inferences:

- Look for a situation in the text in which the author gives clues but doesn't state exactly what is happening.
- Think about what you already know about the situation.
- Combine the text clues with your own experiences or knowledge to make an inference.

▶ **Complete this chart to make an inference about the article "Ruby Bridges."**

What I Learned From Reading

- White parents would not let their children be in Ruby's class.
- Ruby's principal treated her unfairly.
- Ruby's father was fired from his job.

My Inference

_____

_____

_____

_____

_____

_____

What I Already Know

_____

_____

_____

_____

_____

Through

 The Key Idea

▶ **WRITE** What is this autobiography mostly about?

_____

_____

_____

_____

VOCABULARY

◎ **Target Word**

surround

sur•round (verb)

Rate It: ① ② ③ ④

Meaning

to be _____

or _____ *of something*

Example

_____

surrounds *our schoolyard.*

CRITICAL READING

 Analyze

How did U.S. marshals protect Ruby?

BOX Identify the directions the marshals gave to Ruby and her mother.

⚠ **React and Write**

▶ **WRITE** What can you learn about Ruby Bridges from her photo?

My Eyes

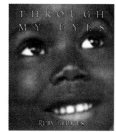

by Ruby Bridges

When Ruby Bridges grew up, she told her story in a book titled *Through My Eyes.* Parts of the book appear here.

November 14, 1960

My mother took special care getting me ready for school. When somebody knocked on my door that morning, my mother saw four serious-looking white men, dressed in suits and wearing armbands. They were U.S. federal marshals. They had come to drive us to school and stay with us all day. I learned later they were carrying guns.

I remember climbing into the back seat of the marshals' car with my mother, but I don't remember feeling frightened. William Frantz Public School was only five blocks away, so one of the marshals in the front seat told my mother right away what we should do when we got there.

"Let us get out of the car first," the marshal said. "Then you'll get out, and the four of us will **surround** you and your daughter. We'll walk up to the door together. Just walk straight ahead, and don't look back." ➤

Words to Know!	**federal** having to do with the government of a whole country

Make Inferences

1. **UNDERLINE** Who came to Ruby's house on her first day of school?

2. ▶ **WRITE** What do you know about why police and other law officers protect people?

_____

_____

_____

_____

3. ▶ **WRITE** What inference can you make about Ruby's safety?

_____

_____

_____

_____

Active Reading

★**STAR** What did people in the crowd do when Ruby arrived at school?

CRITICAL READING

Evaluate

▶**WRITE** Do you think Ruby's mother or the marshals should have told Ruby why there were noisy crowds that day? Why or why not?

_____

_____

_____

_____

_____

_____

React and Write

▶**WRITE** How would you have felt if you were Ruby?

Angry protesters stand across the street from Ruby's school.

When we were near the school, my mother said, "Ruby, I want you to behave yourself today and do what the marshals say."

We drove down North Galvez Street to the point where it crosses Alvar. I remember looking out of the car as we pulled up to the Frantz school. There were barricades and people shouting and policemen everywhere. I thought maybe it was Mardi Gras, the carnival that takes place in New Orleans every year. Mardi Gras was always noisy.

As we walked through the crowd, I didn't see any faces. I guess that's because I wasn't very tall and I was surrounded by the marshals. People yelled and threw things. I could see the school building, and it looked bigger and nicer than my old school. When we climbed the high steps to the front door, there were policemen in uniforms at the top. The policemen at the door and the crowd behind us made me think this was an important place.

It must be college, I thought to myself. ➤

Words to Know! **barricades** barriers to stop people from getting past a certain point

Comprehension Focus
Make Inferences

▶ Complete this chart to make inferences about the autobiography section "November 14, 1960."

What I Learned From Reading

Ruby thought the crowd might be celebrating Mardi Gras.

My Inference

What I Already Know

💡 Active Reading

▶ **WRITE** How did Ruby spend her first day of school?

_____

_____

◎ VOCABULARY
Target Word

confusion

con•fu•sion (noun)

Rate It: ① ② ③ ④

Meaning

the state of _____

something

Example

_____

caused **confusion** for students.

🧠 CRITICAL READING
Synthesize

▶ **WRITE** Brainstorm ideas for another good title for this Workshop. Circle the new title you think is best.

• _____

• _____

• _____

ⓘ React and Write

▶ **WRITE** What do you think Ruby was thinking about when she sat in the office?

The First Day at William Frantz

Once we were inside the building, the marshals walked us up a flight of stairs. The school office was at the top. My mother and I went in and were told to sit in the principal's office. The marshals sat outside. There were windows in the room where we waited. That meant everybody passing by could see us. I remember noticing everyone was white.

All day long, white parents rushed into the office. They were upset. They were arguing and pointing at us. When they took their children to school that morning, the parents hadn't been sure whether William Frantz would be integrated that day or not. After my mother and I arrived, they ran into classrooms and dragged their children out of the school. From behind the windows in the office, all I saw was **confusion**. I told myself that this must be the way it is in a big school.

That whole first day, my mother and I just sat and waited. We didn't talk to anybody. I remember watching a big, round clock on the wall. When it was 3:00 and time to go home, I was glad. I had thought my new school would be hard, but the first day was easy.

Ruby and her mother leave William Frantz after the first day of school.

My First White Teacher

On the second day, my mother and I drove to school with the marshals. The crowd outside the building was ready. Racists spat at us and shouted things. . . .

I tried not to pay attention. When we finally got into the building, my new teacher was there to meet us. Her name was Mrs. Henry. She was young and white. ➤

Words to Know!	**racists** people who believe that some races of people are better than others

Make Inferences

1. **UNDERLINE** Find a detail that shows that Ruby had an unusual first day of school.

2. ▶ **WRITE** How was Ruby different from other students at William Frantz?

_____

_____

_____

3. ▶ **WRITE** Why was Ruby's first day of school so unusual?

_____

_____

_____

_____

_____

Active Reading

★**STAR** What was strange about Ruby's classroom?

VOCABULARY

Target Word

imitate

im•i•tate (verb)

Rate It: ① ② ③ ④

Meaning

to _____ how someone

_____

Example

I _____ to

imitate a _____

React and Write

▶**WRITE** How would you describe Mrs. Henry? Do you think she was a good teacher for Ruby?

Summarize

In one or two sentences, summarize the topic and important details in "Through the Winter With Mrs. Henry."

I had not spent time with a white person before, so I was uneasy at first. Mrs. Henry led us upstairs to the second floor. As we went up, we hardly saw anyone else in the building. The white students were not coming to class. The halls were so quiet, I could hear the noise the marshals' shoes made on the shiny hardwood floors.

Mrs. Henry took us into a classroom and said to have a seat. When I looked around, the room was empty. There were rows of desks, but no children. I thought we were too early, but Mrs. Henry said we were right on time. My mother sat down at the back of the room. I took a seat up front, and Mrs. Henry began to teach.

Through the Winter With Mrs. Henry

After Christmas, my teacher and I settled into a routine. It was odd to be the only child in class, but I finally decided this was the way it was going to be here at the Frantz school. Being Mrs. Henry's only student wasn't a chore. It was fun and felt sort of special. She was more like my best friend than just an ordinary teacher. She was a loving person, and I knew she cared about me.

Mrs. Henry and I always had fun. We did everything together, reading and word puzzles, spelling and math. We sang songs and played games. Since I couldn't go outside, we pushed desks out of the way and did jumping jack exercises.

Words to Know! **routine** a regular way of doing things

Ruby Bridges finished first grade at William Frantz Public School.

I know now that Mrs. Henry influenced me a great deal that year. She had a polite, kind manner that I admired. In fact, I began to **imitate** her. Little by little, I grew to love Mrs. Henry. We became very attached to each other.

The End of First Grade

Near the end of the year, Mrs. Henry and I finally had company. A few white children began coming back to school, and I got an opportunity to visit with them once or twice. Even though these children were white, I still knew nothing about racism or integration. I had picked up bits and pieces over the months from being around adults and hearing them talk, but nothing was clear to me. ➤

Fact and Opinion

1. UNDERLINE A fact is a statement that can be proven. Mark one fact about Ruby's day with Mrs. Henry.

2. CIRCLE An opinion tells what someone thinks. It may seem correct, but it cannot be proven. Mark one of Ruby's opinions about Mrs. Henry.

REVIEW
Compare and Contrast

1. ▶ WRITE Reread page 247. How did the crowd outside the school treat Ruby?

_____

_____

_____

2. ▶ WRITE How did Mrs. Henry treat Ruby?

_____

_____

_____

Active Reading

★**STAR** How does Ruby's school year end?

VOCABULARY

 Target Word

finally

fi•nal•ly *(adverb)*

Rate It: ① ② ③ ④

Meaning

after a _____

Example

After driving for hours, we

finally _____

CRITICAL READING

Synthesize

▶ **WRITE** According to the reading and the time line, how are Ruby Bridges and Jackie Robinson alike?

_____

_____

_____

React and Write

▶ **WRITE** If you were Ruby Bridges, would you want to go back to the same school for second grade? Why or why not?

The light dawned one day when a little white boy refused to play with me. At that moment, it all made sense to me. I **finally** realized that everything had happened because I was black. I remember feeling a little stunned. It was all about the color of my skin. I wasn't angry at the boy, because I understood. His mother had told him not to play with me, and he was obeying her. I would have done the same thing. If my mama said not to do something, I didn't do it.

The next thing I knew, it was June. That incredible year was over. Oddly enough, it ended quietly. I don't remember any special good-byes as I headed off for summer vacation. I was sorry to leave Mrs. Henry, but I somehow thought she would be my teacher again in the fall and forever.

Mrs. Henry gave me excellent grades at the end of the year, but I was told that the school principal threatened to change them. She said I had received so much individual attention that the grades weren't accurate. Mrs. Henry was angry and quarreled with the principal. Mrs. Henry was sad for me and very upset that the principal could be so mean to me. I don't know to this day whether the grades were changed or not. But it didn't matter. The principal couldn't change what was in my head. END

Words to Know! **realized** understood

TEXT FEATURE Reading a Time Line

Key Events in Civil Rights History

1947

Jackie Robinson

Jackie Robinson starts playing for the Brooklyn Dodgers baseball team. This leads to the end of segregation in the sport.

1954

Brown v. Board of Education

The Supreme Court rules that school segregation is unfair. Schools must integrate.

1960

Ruby Bridges

Ruby Bridges integrates her elementary school in New Orleans, Louisiana.

1964

Civil Rights Act

President Lyndon B. Johnson signs the Civil Rights Act of 1964. This ends segregation in all public places.

A time line shows key events in the order in which they happened.

❶ **Analyze:** What is the topic of this time line?

Ⓐ President Lyndon B. Johnson's life

Ⓒ key events in Civil Rights history

Ⓑ *Brown v. Board of Education*

Ⓓ the life of Ruby Bridges

❷ When did Jackie Robinson join the Brooklyn Dodgers?

Ⓐ 1947   Ⓑ 1954   Ⓒ 1960   Ⓓ 1964

❸ Who signed the Civil Rights Act?

Ⓐ Jackie Robinson

Ⓒ Ruby Bridges

Ⓑ President Lyndon B. Johnson

Ⓓ the Supreme Court

✓ Skills Check

1. UNDERLINE Find a detail that tells what the principal did at the end of the year.

2. ▶ WRITE Why do some people treat others unfairly like this?

_____

_____

_____

_____

3. ▶ WRITE What can you infer about the way the principal felt about Ruby?

_____

_____

_____

Meet the Author

RUBY BRIDGES
Born: September 8, 1954, in Mississippi

Early Life: Ruby Bridges was one of the first African-American children to integrate a white school. At just six years old, she was a major figure in the Civil Rights Movement.

Inspiring Others: When she was older, she wrote *Through My Eyes,* a book about her experiences. She also started the Ruby Bridges Foundation to help stop racism. She gives speeches about race issues and civil rights.

Active Reading

CIRCLE Identify three animals that don't frighten the speaker of this poem.

 Craft and Structure

Text Structure Poets often arrange words or lines in a poem to create rhythm or to make a point. Read aloud "Life Doesn't Frighten Me." Pay attention to how short many of the lines are.

▶ **WRITE** What effects does the poet create with these short lines?

_____

_____

_____

_____

_____

_____

 React and Write

▶ **WRITE** What makes you feel frightened? How do you react when you are afraid?

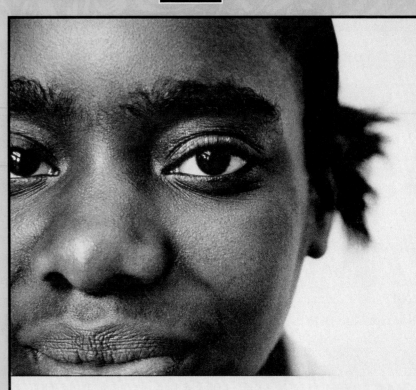

Life Doesn't Frighten Me

by Maya Angelou

Shadows on the wall
Noises down the hall
Life doesn't frighten me at all
Bad dogs barking loud
Big ghosts in a cloud
Life doesn't frighten me at all.

Mean old Mother Goose
Lions on the loose
They don't frighten me at all
Dragons breathing flame
On my counterpane
That doesn't frighten me at all.

I go boo
Make them shoo
I make fun
Way they run
I won't cry
So they fly
I just smile
They go wild
Life doesn't frighten me at all.

Tough guys in a fight
All alone at night
Life doesn't frighten me at all.

Panthers in the park
Strangers in the dark
No, they don't frighten me at all.

That new classroom where
Boys all pull my hair
(Kissy little girls
With their hair in curls)
They don't frighten me at all.

Don't show me frogs and snakes
And listen for my scream,
If I'm afraid at all
It's only in my dreams.

I've got a magic charm
That I keep up my sleeve,
I can walk the ocean floor
And never have to breathe.

Life doesn't frighten me at all
Not at all
Not at all.
Life doesn't frighten me at all.

 **Craft and Structure**

Speaker A poem's speaker is a character that the poet creates to tell the story.

✔**CHECK** What grade in school is the speaker in this poem likely in?

❏ Grade 4
❏ Grade 12
❏ college senior

Repetition is the repeated use of words, phrases, or sentences. Poets use repetition to call attention to an important idea or topic.

UNDERLINE Mark the phrases that repeat in the poem.

Cross-Text Analysis

▶**WRITE** How does this poem's speaker remind you of Ruby Bridges?

_____

_____

_____

Meet the Author

MAYA ANGELOU
Born: April 4, 1928, in St. Louis, Missouri

Life: In her early years, Angelou was a dancer. In 1960 she joined Harlem Writers Guild and got involved in black activism. She is an active poet, author, and playwright.

Career: *I Know Why the Caged Bird Sings* is the first of five autobiographical books. In 1993 she read her poem "On the Pulse of Morning" to the nation at President Clinton's swearing-in ceremony.

Word CHALLENGE

START

1

Choose one. Which activity would you *most* like an **opportunity** to do?

- ☐ visit the moon
- ☐ star in a movie
- ☐ climb a mountain
- ☐ dive off a high board

2 Noun Endings

To show more than one person, place, or thing, add -s to most nouns.

- If a noun ends in *ss, s, x, ch,* or *sh,* add -es to make it plural. Examples: *buses, dresses.*

- If a noun ends in a consonant and *y,* change *y* to *i* and add -es to make the noun plural. Examples: *puppies,* **opportunities**.

- Watch out for irregular plural nouns like *mice,* the plural of *mouse,* and *children,* the plural of *child.* These don't follow the rules!

Write the plural form of each noun.

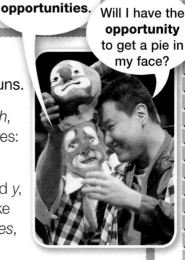

> As a clown, you will have **opportunities**.

> Will I have the **opportunity** to get a pie in my face?

Singular	Plural	Singular	Plural
teacher	_____	box	_____
dress	_____	goose	_____
bench	_____	penny	_____

3

Evaluate. How much does a job matter? Mark two jobs you would **admire** someone for doing.

- ☐ bus driver
- ☐ nurse
- ☐ thief
- ☐ famous singer

4

Finish them. Use **finally** and **surrounded** to complete these sentences.

I had a weird experience this morning. First, I

thought I was _____ by chirping

birds. I _____ realized it was just the

alarm clock on my cell phone. Freaky!

5

Think it over. When would you really need to be **serious**?

☐ taking a test

☐ playing dodgeball

☐ at a family party

☐ talking to your doctor

6

Decide. Write **H** next to anything that is hard to **ignore**. Write **E** next to each thing that is easy to **ignore**.

____ water dripping in the sink while you're reading

____ a classmate who **imitates** you in the lunchroom

____ silly music in an elevator

____ teasing from a sister or brother

7

Match them. Which one on the left is most likely to be **frightened** by each creature on the right? Draw a line to match each pair.

mouse	**spider**
child	**monster**
fly	**cat**

8 Using a Dictionary

Guide words are the words on the top of dictionary pages. They tell the first and last words listed on those pages.

Write each Target Word next to the pair of words that could be its guide words:

admire   frightened   finally

abandon ➤ assist

ad•mire

(ad-**mire**) *verb* **1.** To like and respect someone. *I admire my teacher.*
2. To look at something and enjoy it. *Luis admired the painting.*

Guide Words	Target Words
film / finger	_____
achieve / average	_____
flight / fuel	_____

9

Evaluate. Who has the most **influence** on your life? Check two.

the President of the United States

☐ your principal

☐ the local weather person

☐ a police officer

☐ your classmates

10

Check them. Which situations would cause *you* a lot of **confusion**?

☐ a sudden, huge rainstorm

☐ new hours at the library

☐ new road signs all over town

☐ a blackout

FINISH

Writing Text Type
Personal Narrative

A **personal narrative** tells a story about an experience in the writer's life.

▶ Read José Vargas's personal narrative about a time when he had to be brave.

Student Model

Introduction

An **introductory statement** identifies the topic of the essay and establishes the point of view.

1. <u>UNDERLINE</u> the **introductory statement**.

Body

Body paragraphs describe events in **time order**.

2. **NUMBER** events 1–5 in **time order**.

Sensory details describe how things looked, sounded, felt, smelled, and tasted.

3. ✔**CHECK** six **sensory details**.

Language Use

Dialogue shows exactly what people in the story said.

4. BOX two lines of dialogue.

Linking words and phrases connect ideas and details.

5. CIRCLE five **linking words or phrases**.

Conclusion

The **conclusion** sums up the experience and its effect on the writer.

6. ★ STAR the **conclusion**.

Calm Under Pressure
by José Vargas

One day, my mother had an asthma attack as we arrived home from the park. I was scared, but I knew what to do.

First, I asked Mom if she was okay. She didn't answer. Her face was red. She gasped for breath and pointed at the phone.

Right away, I called 911. "My mom is having an asthma attack," I told the operator in a shaky voice. He asked for my address. He said an ambulance was already on the way. "Tell the driver to hurry," I begged, holding back tears.

Soon, the paramedics arrived. They gave Mom some medication, and oxygen from a metal tank. Finally, she started breathing easier. I sighed with relief. Mom seemed better, but the paramedics wanted a doctor to check her. We rode to the hospital in an ambulance. The emergency room doctor said I might have saved Mom's life. Mom said she admired my bravery.

I was proud that I did not panic during this emergency. Now I know I can stay calm under pressure.

B I U

P 1

Analyze the Text Type

▶ **Work with a partner to understand the purpose and form of a personal narrative.**

Purpose: Personal Narrative
The purpose of a personal narrative is to _____ _____

Introduction

The **introductory statement** of a personal narrative identifies _____ _____

Student Model In his introduction, José identifies the topic as _____ _____

Body

The **body** paragraphs:

1. _____ in time order.

2. include sensory details that describe _____ _____

Student Model

1. The first event José describes is _____

2. A sensory detail in José's first body paragraph is _____ _____

Conclusion

The **conclusion** sums up _____

Student Model José sums up the experience by saying _____ _____ _____

Brainstorm

▶ Read the writing prompt. Use the idea web to help you brainstorm writing ideas.

School

Home

Writing Prompt:
Write an essay about a time
when you had to be brave.

Doctor's Office

Someplace Else

Choose Your Topic

▶ Select one of your ideas from the idea web. Then complete the sentence.

I am going to write about _____

_____ because this experience taught me that _____

_____

Organize Ideas for Writing

▶ **Complete this outline with notes for your personal narrative.**

I. Introduction Introduce your experience and the lesson it taught you.

Once, _____

_____

This experience taught me that _____

_____

II. Body Decide what events each body paragraph will tell. Write a topic sentence for each paragraph. List sensory details for that part of the story.

A. Event _____

_____

    Detail 1: _____

    Detail 2: _____

B. Event _____

_____

    Detail 1: _____

    Detail 2: _____

C. Event _____

_____

    Detail 1: _____

    Detail 2: _____

III. Conclusion Sum up the experience and the effect it had on you.

This experience taught me that _____

_____

_____

_____

_____

_____

Write Your Draft

► **Write a draft of your personal narrative.**

Writing Prompt:
Write an essay about a time when you had to be brave.

WORD CHOICES	
Everyday	**Precise**
change	adjust
do	achieve
event	incident
show	demonstrate

_____
(title)

Introduction

> ► **Write your introductory statement. Identify the experience that is the topic of your essay.**
>
> _____
>
> _____
>
> _____
>
> _____
>
> _____

► **Type your introduction on the computer or write it on paper. Then use some of these linking words and phrases to complete a draft of your essay.**

Body

The first thing . . .	The second thing . . .
At first, . . .	Lastly, . . .
Soon, I . . .	After that, . . .
Then, . . .	Finally, . . .
Next, . . .	Later, . . .

Conclusion

When it was over, . . .	Looking back now, . . .
In the end, . . .	The next time . . .

Revise Your Essay

▶ **Evaluate: Rate your personal narrative. Then have a writing partner rate it.**

Scoring Guide			
needs improvement	average	good	excellent
1	2	3	4

1. **UNDERLINE** the introductory statement. Does it state the topic?
   Self   1   2   3   4
   Partner   1   2   3   4

2. **NUMBER** events in time order. Are the events in the right order?
   Self   1   2   3   4
   Partner   1   2   3   4

3. ✔**CHECK** sensory details. Do they describe the experience?
   Self   1   2   3   4
   Partner   1   2   3   4

4. BOX dialogue. Does it show the exact words that people spoke?
   Self   1   2   3   4
   Partner   1   2   3   4

5. CIRCLE linking words and phrases. Do they connect ideas?
   Self   1   2   3   4
   Partner   1   2   3   4

6. ★**STAR** the conclusion. Does it sum up the experience and its effect on the writer?
   Self   1   2   3   4
   Partner   1   2   3   4

▶ **Discuss: Give feedback on your partner's personal narrative.**

1. Start with a positive comment about your partner's personal narrative.

   A strong part of your narrative is _____

   _____

   I enjoyed reading about _____

   _____

2. Give suggestions for revision.

   I have a question about _____

   _____

   This event would be clearer if _____

   _____

   Your narrative needs to include _____

   _____

3. Answer any questions your partner has about your suggestions.

4. Ask your partner for feedback. Use the frames below to summarize your partner's feedback.

   A strong part of my narrative was . . .
   You had a question about . . .
   The first event would be clearer if . . .
   I need to add . . .

▶ **Revise: Now revise your personal narrative.**

Grammar USING ADVERBS

An **adjective** describes a person, place, or thing. An **adverb** describes a verb, adjective, or another adverb. Many adverbs end in *-ly*.

• Use adverbs to make your writing more precise.

Examples

Adjective	Adverb
Ruby went to a **different** school.	She was treated **differently** from whites.
There were **unfair** laws in many states.	Protesters fought against laws that were **highly** unfair.
Some protesters showed **incredible** bravery.	They acted **incredibly** bravely.

▶ **Circle the correct form of the word in brackets in the sentences below. Write whether you've circled an adjective or an adverb.**

1. Ruby waited [patient patiently] in the office. *adverb*

2. People were [angry angrily] when Ruby arrived at school.

3. Her first day at school passed [slowly slow].

4. Ruby learned [quick quickly] at her new school.

5. Mrs. Henry was very [politely polite] to Ruby.

6. Other students [final finally] returned to school.

▶ **Rewrite the sentences using the correct form of the adverb.**

7. The laws changed slow in some states.

8. Ruby's family took education serious.

9. Students should all be treated equal.

10. Some whites responded violent to integration.

▶ **Edit Your Draft.** Reread each sentence in your draft. **Are adverbs used correctly?** Fix any mistakes you have made with adverbs.

Mechanics USING QUOTATION MARKS

Quotation marks show the exact words, or dialogue, of a speaker.

- The first word of a quotation is usually capitalized.
- Punctuation usually goes inside the second quotation.

Examples

Correct	Incorrect
Annie asked, "Where is the milk?"	Annie asked, "where is the milk?"
"I put it on the table," Yvonne said.	"I put it on the table", Yvonne said.

▶ **Find and correct five errors in this paragraph.**

Student Model

CHECK AND CORRECT

☐ **UNDERLINE** one incorrectly formed adverb and correct it.

☐ Insert two missing quotation marks.

☐ **CIRCLE** two spelling errors and correct them.

Last June, I learned how to swim. Mom enrolled me in swim classes without telling me first! "Don't you know how fritened of water I am? I asked.

"It's important that you learn to swim, Mom insisted. At the first lesson, the teacher gave me floats for my arms. He taught me to kick. After eight lessons, I was swimming like a fish! It was definite the most serius challenge I ever faced!

▶ **Edit Your Draft.** Take a close look at each sentence in your draft. **Are all the quotations punctuated correctly?** Fix any that are not.

Final Draft/Present

▶ Write a final draft of your personal narrative on paper or the computer. Check it again and correct any errors before you present it.

Analyze a Photograph

A photograph captures a moment in time. This is a photo of Elizabeth Eckford, one of nine African-American students to integrate Little Rock High School in Arkansas in 1957.

▶ **Look at the photograph and answer the questions below.**

> **MARK IT**
> * **CIRCLE** the main subject of the photo.
> * **BOX** three faces that express strong feelings.
> * ★**STAR** a part of the photograph that captures your attention.

❶ **In the photo, Elizabeth Eckford looks**

   Ⓐ relaxed.   Ⓒ confused.

   Ⓑ determined.   Ⓓ exhausted.

❷ **This is one of the most famous photos of its time. What are two clues that tell you this is not a recent photo?**

_____

_____

_____

_____

❸ **Six years after this photo was taken, the yelling woman behind Elizabeth contacted her. She apologized for how she acted on that day. If you were Elizabeth, how do you think you would react?**

_____

_____

_____

_____

Filmmaker
Shola Lynch

This filmmaker made a documentary film about Shirley Chisholm, an African-American Congresswoman who ran for U.S. president.

▶ **Read the interview and job information. Then answer questions about Shola Lynch's career.**

S **Scholastic: Were you artistic or creative as a child?**

Shola Lynch: Every year, I created a collage (a collection of pictures) on my bedroom wall. I didn't know it at the time, but collecting meaningful images is an important part of my job as a filmmaker!

S **How did you choose photos for your film?**

I made a point of choosing images that showed the many sides of this interesting woman. Shirley Chisholm was a politician and an activist. She was also a wife and a teacher. She liked to smile and dance.

S **What made you choose Ms. Chisholm as the topic of your film?**

Ms. Chisholm was the first black woman to run for president. I wanted her story to be known by everyone.

❶ **Shola analyzes photographs as part of her job. How did she decide which photos to use in her film?**

_____

_____

❷ **How interesting do you think Shola's job is? Mark the line.**

👎 •——•——•——•——• 👍
   1   **2**   **3**   **4**   **5**
Not very interesting   **Very interesting**

❸ **I think Shola's job is/isn't** (circle one) **interesting because**

_____

_____

ON THE JOB

LOCATION
New York, New York

EDUCATION
Bachelor's degree in Film

RESPONSIBILITIES
• Raises money for films
• Directs a team

SKILLS
• Creativity
• Leadership

SALARY
Experienced filmmakers make $30,000–$135,000.

FAVORITE PART OF THE JOB
"As a documentary filmmaker, I have an excuse to talk to anybody!"

CAREER CONNECTION

Arts, A/V Technology, and Communications
www.careerclusters.org

Related Jobs
• film producer
• actor
• camera operator

What was Ruby's first day like?

As a first grader, Ruby Bridges integrated an all-white school. Write a first-person narrative paragraph **about Ruby's first day. Write from the point of view of someone else at William Frantz Public School.**

❶ **Recall events.** Look back at Reading 2, Ruby's autobiography, and find events that happened on her first day of school. Take notes here.

A. _____

B. _____

C. _____

D. _____

E. _____

❷ **Think creatively.** *Through My Eyes* is told from Ruby's point of view. What might other people have been feeling or thinking on that historic day? Write your ideas.

A. Ruby's mom: _____

_____

B. Mrs. Henry: _____

_____

C. A federal marshal: _____

_____

D. Other: _____

_____

❸ **Choose a point of view.** Choose a narrator (a person who describes events) for your paragraph. Circle that person in the list above.

❹ **Write your paragraph.** Write at least five sentences to tell about your narrator's experiences, thoughts, and feelings on Ruby's first day. Be sure to include:

A. an introductory sentence that uses the word *I*

B. linking words such as *then, also,* and *after*

C. a concluding sentence that sums up your narrator's point of view

AN EFFECTIVE PRESENTATION
✓ is short and focused.
✓ is delivered with expression.
✓ considers the audience.

When Ruby came to William Frantz Public School, I was_____

_____

The first time I saw her, I thought _____

_____

As she made her way through the crowd, _____

_____

_____

_____

_____

_____

_____

_____

_____

❺ **Present effectively.** Read your narrative paragraph to a group. Use these tips as you prepare your presentation.

• Practice reading aloud your paragraph two or three times, until you are comfortable reading it for others.

• At the end of each sentence, make eye contact with members of your audience.

• Read with feeling. Slow down during the important parts and use your voice to stress important moments in the paragraph.

Comprehension

▶ **Fill in the circle next to the correct answer.**

1. Why was Ruby Bridges chosen to go to William Frantz Public School?

 Ⓐ She was chosen because she was so brave.

 Ⓑ Ruby lived very close to that school.

 Ⓒ She did well on a test given at the end of kindergarten.

 Ⓓ Her best friends went there.

CRITICAL READING

2. Evaluate: What serious problem did Ruby have in first grade?

 Ⓐ She had a long argument with her best friend.

 Ⓑ She faced discrimination from white adults.

 Ⓒ There was no one to walk her to school.

 Ⓓ She did not get along well with her teacher.

> **Here's a Tip.**
> To check your answer to a question about a text, reread the text. Circle a detail that supports your answer.

3. Which words best describe Mrs. Henry, Ruby's first-grade teacher?

 Ⓐ kind and loving

 Ⓑ lazy and careless

 Ⓒ strict and unfair

 Ⓓ doubtful and confused

CRITICAL READING

4. Synthesize: The poet Maya Angelou probably wrote "Life Doesn't Frighten Me" to _____.

 Ⓐ make readers have bad dreams

 Ⓑ remember what Ruby Bridges did

 Ⓒ make fun of readers' fears

 Ⓓ help readers to feel brave

5. Analyze: How are Ruby Bridges and the speaker of the poem similar?

 Ⓐ They both make new friends.

 Ⓑ They are both brave in the face of fear.

 Ⓒ They are both heroes of the Civil Rights Movement.

 Ⓓ They both like their teacher.

Vocabulary

▶ **Fill in the circle next to the correct definition of the underlined word.**

1. The crowds outside the school made Ruby feel <u>frightened</u>.

Ⓐ excited   Ⓒ quiet

Ⓑ afraid   Ⓓ angry

2. Ruby's story can <u>influence</u> people to stand up for what is right.

Ⓐ treat unfairly   Ⓒ frustrate

Ⓑ make happy   Ⓓ affect

3. He had a <u>serious</u> look on his face while taking the test.

Ⓐ thoughtful and solemn   Ⓒ clever and funny

Ⓑ sneaky and dangerous   Ⓓ brave and happy

▶ **Choose the correct plural ending for the underlined word.**

4. Ruby's parents knew that a better school would give Ruby more <u>opportunity</u>.

Ⓐ opportunitism   Ⓒ opportunities

Ⓑ opportunitys   Ⓓ correct as is

▶ **Which are the most likely dictionary guide words for the underlined word?**

5. Many people <u>admire</u> Ruby Bridges for her bravery.

Ⓐ *about* and *zipper*   Ⓒ *goat* and *sing*

Ⓑ *addition* and *average*   Ⓓ *expect* and *courage*

Short Answer

CRITICAL READING

▶ **Analyze: Use what you've read in this Workshop to answer the question. Check your spelling and grammar.**

Why was Ruby Bridges a hero of the Civil Rights Movement?

_____

_____

_____

_____

GLOSSARY

A glossary is a useful tool found at the back of many books. It contains information about key words in the text. Look at the sample glossary entry below.

This is an **entry word**— the word you look up. It is divided into syllables.

The **pronunciation** comes after the entry word. Letters and letter combinations stand for different sounds. The accented syllable is marked in boldfaced letters.

This tells you what **part of speech** the entry word is.

pa•tient (pay-shuhnt)

1. *adjective* Able to wait calmly for a long time. *Tyrone was patient even though his mother was late.*

2. *noun* Someone receiving treatment from a doctor. *Dr. Ruiz's patient recovered quickly from surgery.*

A **number** appears at the beginning of each meaning when more than one meaning is given for the entry word.

Look here to find the **meaning** of the entry word.

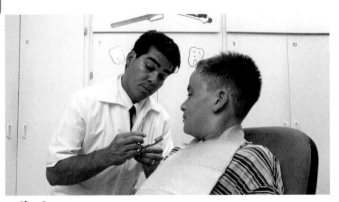

patient

a•ban•don
(uh-**ban**-duhn) *verb*
To leave something you are responsible for. *We were sad when the birds abandoned their eggs in the nest.*

ab•sorb
(ab-**zorb**) *verb*
To soak up liquid. *Use a sponge to absorb all of the extra water.*

a•buse
(uh-**byooss**) *noun*
Harmful treatment. *Some people think that making wild animals do tricks is abuse.*

ac•cu•rate
(**ak**-yuh-ruht) *adjective*
Exactly correct. *The cashier gave me accurate change.*

a•chieve
(uh-**cheev**) *verb*
To succeed in doing something. *Carla works hard to achieve high grades.*

achieve

ad•just
(uh-**juhst**) *verb*
To move or change something slightly. *I adjusted the poster because it was crooked.*

ad•mire
(ad-**mire**) *verb*
1. To like and respect someone. *I admire my teacher and want to do well in her class.*
2. To look at something and enjoy it. *Jon's dad admired the red tie and decided to buy it.*

Suffixes

Admiration ends with the suffix *-tion*. A **suffix** is a letter or group of letters added to the end of a word. The suffix *-tion* changes *admire* from a verb to a noun.

---

af•fect
(uh-**fekt**) *verb*
To influence or change. *My friends affect my attitude toward school.*

ap•peal
(uh-**peel**) *verb*
1. To seem likable or interesting. *Bright colors appeal to little kids.*
2. To ask for something urgently. *I appealed to the doctor for help.*
3. To ask for a decision by a court of law to be changed. *The defense lawyer plans to appeal the verdict of guilty.*

ap•proach
(uh-**prohch**) *verb*
To move nearer. *A big storm might approach our town by noon.*

as•sist•ance
(uh-**siss**-tuhnss) *noun*
Help. *The door was stuck, so I needed assistance to open it.*

at•ten•tion
(uh-**ten**-shuhn) *noun*
1. The act of paying special care to something or someone. *I gave my dog lots of attention after he was hurt in an accident.*
2. Concentration and careful thought. *Sharla paid attention to the directions and did the project correctly.*

a•vail•a•ble
(uh-**vay**-luh-buhl) *adjective*
1. Possible to get. *The new games will be available in stores next week.*
2. Not busy. *I'm available to baby-sit this weekend.*

av•er•age
(**av**-uh-rij)
1. *adjective* Usual, or ordinary. *My brother is of average height.*
2. *noun* Based on a calculation that shows what usually happens. *On average, women live longer than men.*
3. *noun* The number calculated by adding a group of figures together and then dividing the sum by the number of figures. *The average of 2, 5, and 14 is 7.*

bar•ri•cade
(**ba**-ruh-kade) *noun*
A barrier to stop people from getting past a certain point. *The workers put up a barricade to stop people from entering the construction site.*

cap•ture
(**kap**-chur) *verb*
To take a person, animal, or place by force. *The police were able to capture the thief.*

cen•tu•ry
(**sen**-chuh-ree) *noun*
A period of one hundred years. *The castle was built many centuries ago.*

chal•lenge
(**chal**-uhnj) *noun*
Something that is difficult to do. *Ashley loves the challenge of learning to play the piano.*

com•mo•tion
(kuh-**moh**-shuhn) *noun*
Noisy, excited activity. *The President caused a commotion when he walked into the restaurant.*

com•plex
1. (kuhm-**pleks**)
adjective With many parts. *The puzzle was very complex with many small pieces.*
2. (**kom**-pleks) *noun* A group of buildings that are close together and used for the same purpose. *Our apartment is in the building at the back of the complex.*

Multiple-Meaning Words

Complex means "with many parts." It also means "a group of buildings." **Multiple-meaning words** are words that have more than one meaning.

con•cerned
(kuhn-**surnd**) *adjective*
Worried or anxious. *André was concerned that we wouldn't finish our project in time.*

con•di•tion
(kuhn-**dish**-uhn) *noun*
The general state of a person, animal, or thing. *The house was in terrible condition, with broken windows and peeling paint.*

con•fu•sion
(kuhn-**fyoo**-shuhn) *noun*
The state of not understanding something. *Zach caused a lot of confusion when he erased the instructions from the board.*

con•sid•er•ate
(kuhn-**sid**-uh-rit) *adjective*
Thoughtful. *It was considerate of my sister to turn down her music when I went to sleep.*

considerate

con•struct
(kuhn-**struhkt**) *verb*
To build something. *The city plans to construct a new highway by the end of the year.*

con•vince
(kuhn-**vinss**) *verb*
To make someone believe you. *Jack convinced me that he knew the directions to the library.*

cred•it
(**kred**-it) *noun*
Approval or praise for doing something. *My friend and I shared the credit for our project's success.*

cul•ture
(**kuhl**-chur) *noun*
The art, ideas, and beliefs of a group of people. *I am studying the culture of ancient Greece.*

de•fen•si•ble
(di-**fen**-suh-buhl) *adjective*
Easy to defend against attack. *The army made the fort defensible against the enemy.*

de•gree
(di-**gree**) *noun*
1. A unit for measuring temperature. *The temperature hasn't dropped a degree all day.*
2. A title given by a college or university. *My mom has a law degree.*

de•lay
(di-**lay**) *verb*
1. To make someone or something late. *The storm delayed Mike's plane arrival.*
2. To put off until later. *We will delay dinner by an hour.*

dis•play
(diss-**play**)
1. *verb* To show something. *We will display our projects at the end of class.*
2. *noun* A public show or exhibition. *My trophies were put on display at school.*

display

doubt
(**dout**) *verb*
To not believe something. *I doubt my sister will remember my birthday this year.*

en•cour•age
(en-**kur**-ij) *verb*
To praise or offer support. *My friends always encourage me to do my best.*

en•er•gy
(**en**-ur-jee) *noun*
1. The strength to do things without getting tired. *I took a nap so I would have plenty of energy for the party.*
2. Power. *Turn off the lights when you leave so we don't waste energy.*

e•nor•mous
(i-**nor**-muhss) *adjective*
Very large. *José won an enormous stuffed bear at the carnival.*

en•roll
(en-**rohl**) *verb*
To sign up for. *I plan to enroll in dance classes this summer.*

en•tranced
(en-**transd**) *adjective*
Amazed, enchanted. *I was entranced by the colorful hot air balloons up in the sky.*

es•tab•lish
(ess-**tab**-lish) *verb*
To found or start something. *My dad plans to establish his own business next year.*

ex•am•ine
(eg-**zam**-uhn) *verb*
To look at or study something carefully. *The detective wants to examine the evidence.*

ex•haus•tion
(eg-**zawst**-shuhn) *noun*
The state of being extremely tired. *I didn't get much sleep last night, and now I'm suffering from exhaustion.*

ex•hib•it
(eg-**zib**-it) *noun*
A display in a public place where people can see it. *The museum has a new exhibit on dinosaurs.*

ex•pect
(**ek**-spekt) *verb*
To think something will happen. *I expect to do well on the test.*

ex•pert
(**ek**-spurt) *noun*
Someone with special knowledge or skills. *An expert on school safety spoke to our class today.*

fa•mil•iar
(fuh-**mil**-yur) *adjective*
Already known. *Tessa was happy to see some familiar faces at the park.*

Root Words
The word *familiar* comes from the Latin root *familia* which means "family." A **root** is a word or word part from another language that is the basis of an English word.

fam•ine
(**fam**-uhn) *noun*
Ongoing and widespread hunger. *After the rain ruined the crops, the village faced a serious famine.*

far•ther
(**far**-thur) *adverb*
At a greater distance than something else. *Dad's new job is farther from our house than his last one.*

fed•er•al
(**fed**-ur-uhl) *adjective*
Having to do with the government of a whole country. *The federal government creates many laws for our country.*

Idioms
Someone who gets really upset about something can be "making a *federal* case out of it." "To make a federal case" is an **idiom**, an expression that means something different from the separate words.

fierce
(**fihrss**) *adjective*
Violent and dangerous. *Many animals become fierce if they are trapped.*

fierce

fi•nal•ly
(**fye**-nuhl-lee) *adverb*
After a long time. *The bus finally arrived to take us home from school.*

flee
(**flee**) *verb*
To run away. *The firefighters had to flee the wildfire because it was spreading out of control.*

foot•hill
(**fut**-hil) *noun*
A low hill at the base of a mountain. *The town was in the foothills of Mt. Everest.*

fright•ened
(**frite**-uhnd) *adjective*
Afraid. *I was so frightened after watching the horror movie that I couldn't go to sleep.*

fu•el
(**fyoo**-uhl) *noun*
Something that can be burned. *The car stalled because it was out of fuel.*

gaze
(**gayz**) *verb*
To look at something for a long time. *We gazed in wonder as the sun rose.*

globe
(**glohb**) *noun*
The world; any round object. *Maria wants to travel around the globe.*

grate•ful
(**grayt**-fuhl) *adjective*
Thankful. *Marcus was grateful to Amber for helping him with his homework.*

hab•it
(**hab**-it) *noun*
An activity you do often, without thinking. *Making your bed each morning is a good habit.*

hab•i•tat
(**hab**-uh-tat) *noun*
The natural environment of a plant or animal. *The rain forest is this monkey's habitat.*

ig•nore
(ig-**nor**) *verb*
To take no notice of something. *Liza ignored their rude comments.*

Verb Endings
The past-tense form of *ignore* is *ignored*. The present-tense form is *ignoring*. **Verb endings** show when an action takes place. To show an action in the past, you often can add *-ed*. If a verb ends with the letter *e*, it is usually dropped before adding *-ed* or *-ing*.

im•i•tate
(**im**-uh-tate) *verb*
To copy how someone talks or behaves. *My sister hates when I imitate her.*

im•prove
(im-**proov**) *verb*
To make better. *Kayla wants to improve her math skills.*

in•ci•dent
(**in**-suh-duhnt) *noun*
Something serious or violent that happens. *The police looked into the incident at the mall.*

in•flu•ence
(**in**-floo-uhnss)
1. *verb* To have an effect on someone or something. *My friends influence my choice of clothing.*
2. *noun* The effect someone or something has on someone or something else. *I hope to be a good influence on my younger sister.*

in•jure
(**in**-jur) *verb*
To hurt yourself or someone else. *I fell and injured my foot.*

injure

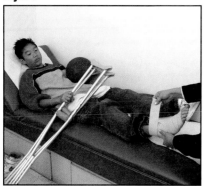

in•sist
(in-**sist**) *verb*
To make a firm demand for or about something. *My parents insist that I come home right after school.*

in•stinct
(**in**-stingkt) *noun*
1. A natural feeling or behavior. *Ducks swim by instinct.*
2. Knowing or feeling something without being told about it. *I had an instinct that she was not telling the truth.*

in•te•grate
(**in**-tuh-grate) *verb*
1. To include people of all races. *In the 1950s, schools in the South began to integrate.*
2. To combine several things into one whole. *Let's integrate our ideas to tell one story.*

in•ves•ti•gate
(in-**vess**-tuh-gate) *verb*
To find out or explore something. *The detectives took three weeks to investigate the case.*

jour•ney
(**jur**-nee) *noun*
A long trip. *My uncle packed four bags for his long journey to China.*

lay•er
(**lay**-ur) *noun*
Something that is placed or exists on or between other things. *I wore a sweater under my coat to add an extra layer of warmth.*

le•gal
(**lee**-guhl) *adjective*
Having to do with the law. *My parents signed many legal papers when they adopted my brother.*

Prefixes
Illegal begins with the prefix *il-*, meaning "not." A **prefix** is a letter or group of letters added to the beginning of a word. A prefix changes the meaning of a word. *Illegal* means "not legal to do something."

lib•er•ty
(**lib**-ur-tee) *noun*
A country's or a person's freedom. *Many people come to the United States for its liberty.*

lo•cate
(**loh**-kate) *verb*
To find something. *Please locate Texas on the map.*

layer

ma•te•ri•al
(mah-**tihr**-ee-uhl) *noun*
Things, such as wood, plastic, or cloth, used to make other things. *The shirt was made from an expensive material.*

meth•od
(**meth**-uhd) *noun*
A way of doing something. *Tina had a special method for making her bed.*

mis•sion
(**mish**-uhn) *noun*
1. A church or other place where aid is given to people in need. *Many refugees went to the mission for food and medical care.*
2. A special job or task. *Our mission is to collect clothing for the flood victims.*

ne•ces•si•ty
(nuh-**sess**-uh-tee) *noun*
A strong need or requirement. *Food and water are basic necessities for life.*

ne•glect
(ni-**glekt**) *verb*
To fail to take care of someone or something. *Pedro neglected his plants so they died.*

nerve
(**nurv**) *noun*
1. Courage. *You need lots of nerve to be a lion tamer.*
2. Boldness or rudeness. *Justin's got a lot of nerve, answering back like that!*
3. One of many thin fibers that send messages from your brain to your body. *Alden's dad suffered damage to a nerve in his shoulder in the car accident.*

nerv•ous
(**nur**-vuhss) *adjective*
Worried or frightened about something. *Thunder and lightning make Vince nervous.*

nor•mal•ly
(**nor**-muhl-lee) *adverb*
Often, or usually. *I normally eat cereal or eggs for breakfast.*

nu•tri•tious
(noo-**trish**-uhss) *adjective*
Healthy to eat. *My parents make a nutritious dinner with lots of vegetables every night.*

ob•vi•ous
(**ob**-vee-uhss) *adjective*
Clear, easy to see. *His frown was an obvious sign that he was unhappy.*

Antonyms
Obvious means "clear and easy to see" and **mysterious** means "not easy to understand." These words are **antonyms**, words that have opposite meanings.

opponent

op•po•nent
(uh-**poh**-nuhnt) *noun*
Someone who is against you in a game. *I shook my opponent's hand after the game.*

op•por•tu•ni•ty
(op-ur-**too**-nuh-tee) *noun*
A chance to do something. *Lynda's job gives her the opportunity to travel.*

pa•tient
(**pay**-shuhnt)
1. *adjective* Able to wait calmly for a long time. *Tyrone was patient even though his mother was late.*
2. *noun* Someone receiving treatment from a doctor. *Dr. Ruiz's patient recovered quickly from surgery.*

per•cent
(pur-**sent**) *noun*
A part of a whole. *Ninety percent of the students voted for Raul when he ran for class president.*

phys•i•cal
(**fiz**-uh-kuhl) *adjective*
Having to do with the body. *In physical education, we learn how to take care of our bodies.*

por•tion
(**por**-shuhn) *noun*
1. An amount of food for one person. *I'd like another portion of string beans.*
2. A part or piece of something. *He spent a large portion of the evening doing his homework.*

pre•fer
(pri-**fur**) *verb*
To like one thing more than another. *Magda prefers oranges to apples.*

pre•serve
(pri-**zurv**)
1. *verb* To keep something from being destroyed. *Let's put the photos in an album to preserve them.*
2. *noun* Jam or jelly. *Derrick loves toast with apricot preserves.*

pres•sure
(**presh**-ur) *noun*
Strong influence, force, or persuasion. *My dad is under pressure to do well at work.*

pre•vi•ous
(**pree**-vee-uhss) *adjective*
Happening before. *I like this school a lot more than my previous one.*

priv•i•lege
(**priv**-uh-lij) *noun*
A special right or advantage. *The President of the United States enjoys the privilege of living in the White House.*

Noun Endings

To show more than one person, place, or thing, add -*s* to most nouns, like ***privileges***. If a noun ends in *s*, add -*es* to make it plural, like *buses*. If a noun ends in *y*, change the *y* to *i* and add -*es*, as in *spies*.

---

pro•ceed
(pruh-**seed**) *verb*
To go ahead with something. *Let's proceed with the meeting even though Alex isn't here yet.*

quiv•er
(**kwiv**-ur) *verb*
To shake. *Jess's voice quivered as she gave her speech.*

rac•ist
(**ray**-sist) *noun*
Someone who believes that some races of people are better than others. *In the 1960s, racists did not want black and white children to go to school together.*

rag•ged•y
(**rag**-eh-dee) *adjective*
Torn and in bad condition. *I wore my favorite skirt so often that it became raggedy.*

range
(**raynj**) *noun*
1. The area where an animal lives and hunts. *We visited a cattle range on our trip.*
2. A line of mountains. *Many of the peaks in the mountain range were covered with snow.*
3. A variety of a group of things. *We could choose from a range of paint colors in art class.*

rap•id•ly
(**rap**-id-lee) *adverb*
Moving very fast or quickly. *He walked rapidly to get to class on time.*

re•al•ize
(**ree**-uh-lize) *verb*
To understand. *Lee realized he was working too hard and needed to take a break.*

re•build
(ree-**bild**) *verb*
To build again. *The city had to rebuild all its offices destroyed by the storm.*

re•gion
(**ree**-juhn) *noun*
A section or part of a place or country. *In which region of the country do you live?*

re•luc•tant•ly
(ri-**luhk**-tuhnt-lee) *adverb*
Not wanting to do something. *She wanted to talk on the phone, but instead reluctantly did her chores.*

re•ly
(ri-**lye**) *verb*
To need and trust someone. *My mom relies on me to take care of my little brother.*

re•move
(ri-**moov**) *verb*
To take away. *Please remove the empty plates from the table.*

re•un•ion
(ree-**yoon**-yuhn) *noun*
A meeting or gathering of people who know each other. *My family is having a big reunion this summer.*

roam
(**rohm**) *verb*
To travel. *Animals like to roam in the wild.*

route
(**root** or **rout**) *noun*
A way to get from one place to another. *I walk the same route to school every day.*

rou•tine
(roo-**teen**) *noun*
A regular way of doing things. *Taking out the garbage is part of my family's daily routine.*

safari

sa•fa•ri
(suh-**fah**-ree) *noun*
A trip taken to see large animals. *Last year, my cousin got to ride an elephant when she went on a safari.*

sat•is•fy
(**sat**-iss-fye) *verb*
To please by giving what someone wants or needs. *My parents were satisfied with my grades this year.*

scrape
(**skrape**) *verb*
To scratch. *I scraped my knee when I fell off my bike.*

seek
(**seek**) *verb*
To look for. *My teacher is seeking an assistant.*

se•lect
(si-**lekt**) *verb*
To choose. *Please select a movie you'd like to watch.*

se•ri•ous
(**sihr**-ee-uhss) *adjective*
1. Thoughtful and solemn. *After we lost the game, everyone was serious on the bus ride home.*
2. Very bad or dangerous. *She has a serious illness.*

source
(**sorss**) *noun*
Where something comes from. *What's the source of this drinking water?*

Synonyms
A *source* is "where something comes from" and *origin* is "the place where something began." These words are **synonyms**, words that have similar meanings.

strength•en
(**strengkth**-uhn) *verb*
To make stronger. *I exercise to strengthen my muscles.*

strug•gle
(**struhg**-uhl) *noun*
A difficult challenge. *Learning to play the clarinet was a struggle for me.*

sur•round
(suh-**round**) *verb*
To be all around or on every side of something. *A fence surrounds the garden.*

sur•vive
(sur-**vive**) *verb*
1. To stay alive during a dangerous event. *Xavier and his family survived the tornado by staying in the basement.*
2. To continue to live or exist. *Humans need food and water to survive.*

sus•pend
(suh-**spend**) *verb*
1. To force to leave school temporarily. *Julie was suspended from school for a week.*
2. To stop something for a short time. *Work was suspended for the holidays.*

sym•bol
(**sim**-buhl) *noun*
A sign or object that represents something else. *On many maps, a small, green pine tree is the symbol for a forest.*

Homophones
Symbol means "an object that represents something else" and *cymbal* means "a musical instrument made of brass, shaped like a plate." These are **homophones**, words that sound alike but have different spellings and meanings.

sys•tem
(siss-tuhm) *noun*
A way of completing a task. *I need a better system for studying.*

task
(task) *noun*
A job, or work to be done. *After the party, my task was picking up all the trash.*

ter•ri•fied
(ter-uh-fyed) *adjective*
Really scared. *I am terrified of dogs.*

threat

threat
(thret) *noun*
A danger that something bad might happen. *A bully is a threat to every student.*

tomb
(toom) *noun*
A burial chamber. *I saw a mummy's tomb at the museum.*

trans•late
(transs-late) *verb*
Change words from one language to another. *Veronica translated the story from English into Spanish.*

trans•port
(transs-**port**) *verb*
To move an object or person. *The truck transported chickens.*

trench
(trench) *noun*
A long, narrow ditch. *The firefighters dug a trench to stop the wildfire from spreading.*

u•nite
(yoo-**nite**) *verb*
1. To bring together; to make whole. *The states united to form one nation.*
2. To join together to achieve something. *Let's unite to change the school rule.*

val•ue
(val-yoo)
1. *noun* What something is worth. *What is the value of this gold watch?*
2. *verb* To think that something is important. *I value Anna's friendship greatly.*

va•ri•e•ty
(vuh-**rye**-uh-tee) *noun*
1. A selection of different items. *I like a variety of music, including rap and pop.*
2. A type of something that is different from others in its group. *Granny Smith is one variety of apple.*

voy•age
(**voi**-ij) *noun*
A long trip, especially by ship or spacecraft. *My aunt packed six suitcases for her voyage across the Atlantic Ocean.*

voyage

worth
(wurth) *adjective*
Useful, desirable, or helpful to do. *It was worth spending time on the project because I learned a lot about electricity.*

Compound Words
Worthwhile is a compound word. A **compound word** is made up of two smaller words, like *worth* + *while*.

How to Use the Reading Handbook

This handbook includes the comprehension skills that you mastered in the *rBook*. You can use these directions and charts to review what you know. You can also use them in your other classes, like social studies and science. They can help you understand a new text or story.

Main Idea and Details

The **main idea** is the most important point about a topic. **Details** are the facts that support the main idea. To find the main idea and details:

- Decide what the topic is. Find the main idea about the topic.
- Look for the details that support the main idea.

▶ **Use this chart to identify a main idea and supporting details.**

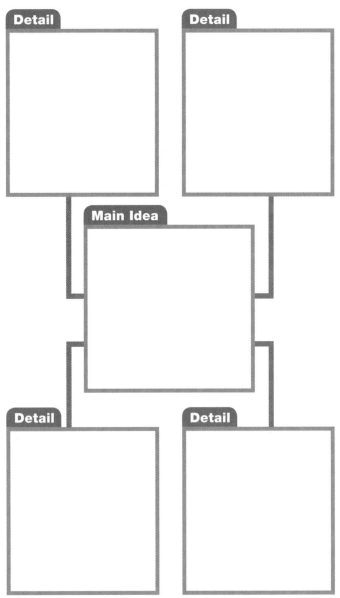

Sequence of Events

Sequence is the order in which events happen. To find the sequence of events:

- Try to remember the order in which events take place.
- Look for times, dates, and signal words such as *first*, *then*, *next*, *after*, and *finally*.
- When you know the order, check it again. Make sure it makes sense.

▶ **Use this chart to identify a sequence of events.**

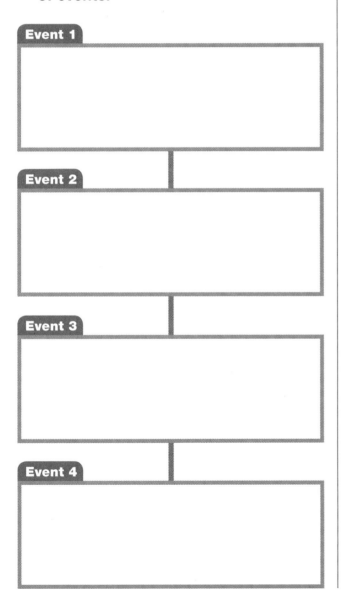

Summarize

A **summary** is a short statement of the most important ideas in a reading. To summarize:

- Find the topic of the reading.
- Look for the most important details about the topic.
- Restate the topic and important details in a short summary. Use your own words.

▶ **Use this chart to identify the topic and important details in a summary.**

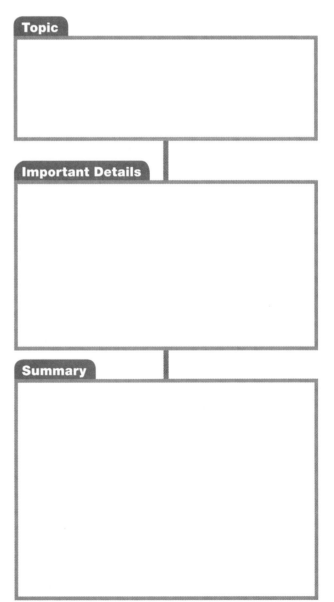

Problem and Solution

A **problem** is a situation or event that causes trouble. A **solution** is what fixes the problem. To find a problem and its solution:

- Look for the problem.
- Find the solution to the problem.

▶ **Use this chart to identify a problem and a solution.**

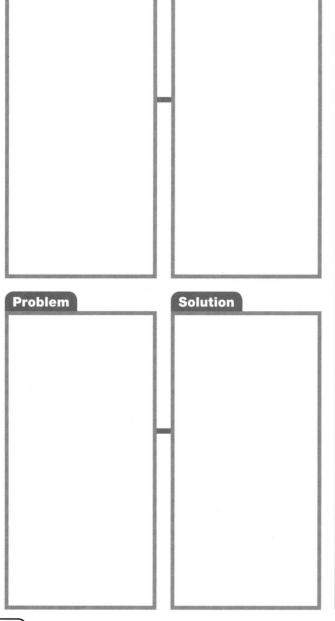

Cause and Effect

A **cause** is the reason something happens. An **effect** is the result of a cause. To find the cause and effect:

- Ask yourself "Why did it happen?" to find the cause.
- Ask yourself "What happened?" to find the effect.
- Look for signal words or phrases such as *because*, *so*, *as a result*, and *for this reason*.

▶ **Use this chart to identify cause-and-effect relationships.**

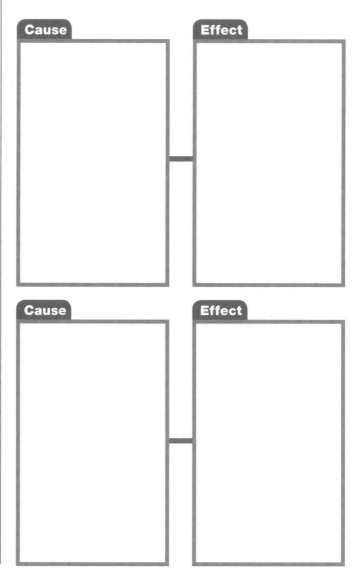

Compare and Contrast

When you **compare**, you tell how two people or things are alike. When you **contrast**, you tell how they are different. To compare and contrast:

- Ask yourself how two people or things are the same. Look for signal words and phrases such as *both*, *like*, *also*, and *in addition*.

- Ask yourself how two people or things are different. Look for signal words such as *unlike*, *but*, *rather than*, and *however*.

▶ **Use this chart to compare and contrast two elements in a reading.**

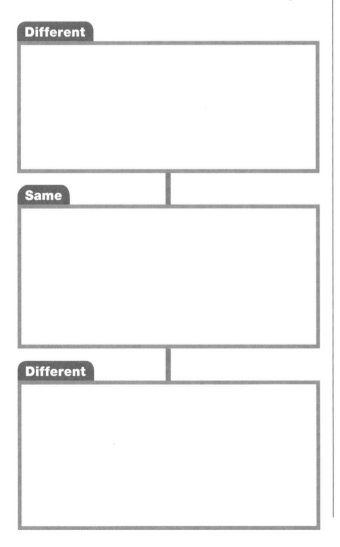

Make Inferences

When you **make inferences**, you form ideas about things that are not directly stated in the text. To make inferences:

- Look for a situation in the text in which the author gives clues but doesn't state exactly what is happening.

- Think about what you already know about the topic.

- Combine the text clues with your own experiences or knowledge to make an inference.

▶ **Use this chart to make an inference.**

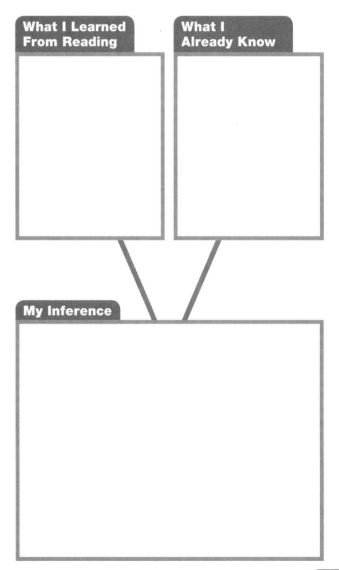

Story Elements

A short story is a brief work of fiction. It focuses on one or two main characters and on a single problem or conflict. To understand a short story, look for four elements:

Setting

Setting is where and when a story takes place. To analyze the setting:

- Look at the illustrations.
- Look for details that tell *where*. Ask yourself, "What words in the story help me imagine what the place looks like?"
- Look for story details that tell *when* and *what time*. Ask yourself, "When does this story take place? Is it long ago, in the future, or in the present?"
- Pay attention to any changes in the setting and how they affect the story.

Character

A **character** is a person or animal in a story. It's who the story is about. Often, stories have several characters. The main characters are the ones the story is mostly about. Characters have special qualities, or traits, that make up their personalities. To analyze a character:

- Look for words the author uses to describe the character, especially adjectives.
- Pay attention to what the character thinks, says, and does.
- Be aware of what other characters say about the main character.
- Think about what you already know about people and their behavior.

Plot

Plot is what happens in a story. It includes a problem that the main character needs to solve, the events leading to a solution, and the solution. To analyze the plot:

- Find out the main character's problem.
- Look at what the character says and does to try to solve the problem.
- Pay attention to events that help solve the problem. Look at what happens that gets in the way of solving the problem.
- Think about how the story turns out. Does the character solve the problem? How?

Theme

The **theme** is the important message about life that the author wants readers to understand. It often helps the reader understand the author's purpose, thoughts, and feelings. To analyze the theme:

- Think about what the characters do and say.
- Think about what happens to the characters.
- Ask yourself, "What does the author want readers to know about life?"

▶ **Use this chart to keep track of the setting, character, plot, and theme of a story you are reading.**

Story Title: _____

	Part 1	Part 2	Part 3
Setting	Time: _____ _____ Places: _____ _____	Time: _____ _____ Places: _____ _____	Time: _____ _____ Places: _____ _____
Character	Who is the main character? _____ Describe him/her: _____ _____	How does the character change? _____ _____ _____	What is the character like now? _____ _____ _____
Plot	What happens at the beginning of the story? _____ _____ _____	What happens in the middle of the story? _____ _____ _____	How does the story end? _____ _____ _____
Theme	Author's message:		

Literary Craft and Structure Terms

author a person who writes a short story, play, poem, novel, article, essay, or book

autobiography a book-length story about one's life written by that person

characters the people or animals in a story

conflict the problem in a story. An internal conflict takes place in the mind of a character who must resolve something. An external conflict takes place between two characters or between a character and a force of nature, society, or the unknown.

dialogue a conversation between characters

fiction a story with imaginary characters, events, and settings

figurative language words that say something other than their literal meaning. Similes and metaphors use figurative language. Example: *All the world's a stage.* (metaphor)

genre a category, or type, of literature, such as fiction, nonfiction, poetry, and drama

historical fiction a story or novel whose setting is some period in the past. Often, real people from the past or important historical events are used in works of historical fiction.

imagery the use of descriptive words and phrases to create pictures, or images, in the reader's mind. Example: *The sunlight sparkled like diamonds on the water.*

metaphor a comparison in which something is said to be something else. Metaphors use *is* or *was*. Example: *She is a shining star.*

mood the general feeling that an author creates. Mood is created largely through description and setting.

narrator the teller of a story. A first-person narrator tells a story using the word *I*.

nonfiction a true story based on real people and factual events

novel a book that tells a story about made-up characters and events and usually has more than one plot, character, setting, and theme

personal narrative a true story about a person's life told in the first person

plot what happens in a story, including the problem, events that lead to solving the problem, and the solution

poetry literature that uses language chosen for its sound and for its ability to express emotion

point of view the perspective from which a story is told. In the **first-person point of view**, the narrator is usually a character in the story. This narrator tells the story by using the pronouns *I* or *we*. In the **third-person point of view**, the narrator may or may not be a character in the story. This narrator uses the pronouns *he*, *she*, *they* and characters' names. Sometimes the narrator in the third-person point of view knows what every character is doing, thinking, and even feeling.

repetition words, phrases, or sentences that are used over and over again

rhyme two or more words that have ending syllables with the same sound

rhythm a regular, repeated pattern of sounds in music or poetry

sensory details descriptive words and phrases that appeal to the reader's sense of sight, hearing, touch, smell, and taste

setting the time and place of a story

short story a brief work of fiction that focuses on one or two main characters and on a single problem

simile a comparison of two unlike things showing one way they are alike and using the words *like* or *as*. Example: *That dinosaur is as big as a house.*

speaker a character or person that a poet creates to tell the story in a poem. The speaker's voice is sometimes very different from the poet's voice.

stanza a group of two or more lines of a poem that are held together by length, rhyme, rhythm (beat) and/or meaning

tone the author's attitude about the subject he or she has written about. An author's writing tone can be formal or informal.

suspense a state of uncertainty that readers feel when they wonder what will happen next in a story and keeps them reading

theme the important message about life that the author wants readers to understand from a story or poem. The theme is revealed by the whole story—by the title, the plot, the characters, the setting, and the mood.

verse words arranged in the form of poetry

How to Use the Writing Handbook

This handbook includes the writing skills that you mastered in the *rBook*. You can use these directions and charts to review what you know. You can also use them to help you with a new writing assignment.

Explanatory Paragraph

An **explanatory paragraph** provides information and explains it.

- State the **topic** in the first sentence and include a **controlling idea**.
- Support the topic with **facts and details**.
- Use **linking words and phrases** to introduce and connect ideas.
- **Sum up** the topic in a **concluding sentence**.

▶ **Use this chart to plan an explanatory paragraph.**

Topic Sentence

Detail 1

Detail 2

Detail 3

Concluding Sentence

Narrative Paragraph

A **narrative paragraph** tells a story about real or imagined events or experiences.

- State the experience and your point of view in the **introductory statement**.
- Describe the events in **time order**.
- Use **sensory details and vivid adjectives** to bring the events to life.
- Use **linking words and phrases** to bring the event to life.
- Tell your feelings about the experience in a **concluding sentence**.

▶ **Use this chart to plan a narrative paragraph.**

Introductory Statement

Event 1

Event 2

Event 3

Concluding Sentence

Literary Analysis Paragraph

In a **literary analysis**, the writer discusses a story's characters, plot, or setting.

- State the **title, author, and text type** in the topic sentence.
- Include a **controlling idea**.
- Give supporting **details, quotes, and examples** from the text.
- Use **linking words and phrases** to connect your details and examples.
- Sum up your key ideas in a **concluding sentence**.

▶ **Use this chart to plan a literary analysis paragraph.**

Topic Sentence

Detail 1

Detail 2

Detail 3

Concluding Sentence

Opinion Essay

An **opinion essay** states an opinion about an issue. Reasons, examples, and facts support the opinion.

- State the issue in an **introductory statement,** and present your opinion in a clear **focus statement.**
- Start each body paragraph with a topic sentence, and include supporting **reasons, examples, and facts.**
- Use **linking words and phrases** to connect the reasons, facts, and ideas.
- Restate the focus statement and give a recommendation in the **conclusion.**

▶ **Use this chart to plan an opinion essay.**

Introduction

Reason/Example 1

Reason/Example 2

Reason/Example 3

Conclusion

Informational Summary

An **informational summary** gives the key topics and ideas from a text.

- State the **title, author, and text type** in an **introductory statement.**
- Include a **focus statement** that tells your plan for the essay.
- Each body paragraph has a **topic sentence,** and includes **details, examples, and quotes** from the text.
- Use **linking words and phrases** to introduce and connect ideas.
- Restate the focus statement in the **conclusion.**

▶ **Use this chart to plan an informational summary.**

Introductory Statement

Body Paragraph 1

Body Paragraph 2

Body Paragraph 3

Conclusion

Literary Analysis Essay

In a **literary analysis**, a writer discusses the character, plot, or setting of a story.

- State the **title, author, and text type** in the introductory statement.
- Include a **focus statement with a controlling idea** that gives a plan for the essay.
- Each body paragraph begins with a topic sentence and includes supporting **details, quotes, and examples**.
- Use **linking words and phrases** to connect details and examples.
- Restate your focus statement in a **concluding sentence**.

▶ **Use this chart to plan a literary analysis essay.**

Introductory Statement

Body Paragraph 1

Body Paragraph 2

Body Paragraph 3

Conclusion

Personal Narrative Essay

A **personal narrative** tells a story about an experience in the writer's life.

- State the experience and give your point of view in an **introductory statement**. Describe the events in **time order**.
- Include **sensory details and your personal thoughts and feelings**.
- Use **linking words and phrases** to connect the ideas and details.
- Tell your feelings about the experience in **a concluding sentence**.

▶ **Use this chart to plan a personal narrative essay.**

Introductory Statement

Body Paragraph 1

Body Paragraph 2

Body Paragraph 3

Conclusion

Research Paper

A **research paper** presents information on a subject gathered from reliable sources.

▶ **Follow these steps before writing your research paper.**

- **Think about the topic.** Ask yourself: What do I want to say about the topic?
- **Research sources.** Gather information from reliable sources. Your sources may include books, websites, encyclopedias, magazines, and news articles.
- **Take notes.** As you research the topic, write down relevant facts and details.
- **Develop a focus statement.** Review your notes. Then write a focus statement that gives a plan for your research paper.
- **Organize your ideas.** Look over your notes and make an outline for your paper. List topic sentences as A, B, and C. Give details under each topic sentence and number them 1, 2, and 3.
- **Cite your sources.** Make sure you give credit to the sources you use in your paper. Any information that you use directly from a reading must be given credit by giving the author's name and the page where it appears.

▶ **Use these tips as you write your research paper.**

- Introduce the topic in an **introductory statement**. Include a **focus statement** that tells what you will explain in the paper.
- Start each body paragraph with a **topic sentence** that has a **controlling idea**.
- Include **facts and examples** that support your focus statement. Use **citations** (author and page) to identify sources.
- Sum up your ideas in the **conclusion**.

▶ **Use this chart to plan a research paper.**

Introduction

Body Paragraph 1

Body Paragraph 2

Body Paragraph 3

Conclusion

Grammar

▶ IDENTIFYING SENTENCES AND FRAGMENTS

A **sentence** is a group of words that tells a complete idea. Every sentence has two parts.

- The **subject** tells who or what the sentence is about.
- The **predicate** tells what someone or something does.

A **sentence fragment** is an incomplete sentence that can't stand by itself. Often, a fragment is missing either a subject or a predicate.

Example

Sentence Fragment	Complete Sentence
wear brightly colored clothes. [missing a subject]	Smoke jumpers wear brightly colored clothes.
In order to burn, fires [missing a predicate]	In order to burn, fires need heat, oxygen, and fuel.

▶ CORRECTING SENTENCE FRAGMENTS

A sentence fragment is an incomplete sentence. Often, sentence fragments are missing a subject or a verb. To fix some fragments, add a subject or verb to make a **complete sentence**.

Example

Sentence Fragment	Complete Sentence
Settlers from Europe. [missing verb]	Settlers came from Europe.
Moved to America. [missing subject]	Settlers moved to America.

To correct some sentence fragments, you can connect the fragment to a complete sentence by adding a comma and any missing words.

Example

Sentence and Fragment	Complete Sentence
Virpal's mom lived in the United States. Her grandma in India. [missing verb]	Virpal's mom lived in the United States, and her grandma lived in India.

▶ CORRECTING RUN-ON SENTENCES

A **run-on sentence** is made up of two complete thoughts that are incorrectly joined together.

- To fix a run-on sentence, separate the ideas into two **complete sentences**.
- Or, insert a comma and a connecting word between the thoughts.

Example

Run-on sentence:	Bud woke up late he ran to get in line.
Complete sentences:	Bud woke up late. He ran to get in line.
Complete sentence:	Bud woke up late, so he ran to get in line.

▶ USING CORRECT VERB TENSE

The **tense** of a verb shows when the action happens.

- A **present-tense verb** shows action that is happening now.
- A **past-tense verb** shows action that took place in the past. Most past-tense verbs end in -*ed*.

Example

Present-Tense Verb	Past-Tense Verb
Bullies pick on some kids. A bully teases my friend.	Bullies picked on my brother. The bully teased her all last year.

Some verbs have irregular past-tense forms. These verbs don't end in -*ed*.

Example

Present-Tense Verb	Past-Tense Verb
I am happy when I see my friends. I often think about my friend who moved away.	I am happy that I saw my friends. Yesterday, I thought about my friend who moved away.

► USING IRREGULAR VERBS

Most past-tense verbs end in *-ed*. **Irregular verbs** do not.

• You must remember the different spellings of irregular past-tense verbs.
• The verb *to be* is a common irregular verb. Its **present-tense** forms are *am*, *is*, *are*. Its past-tense forms are *was*, *was*, *were*.

Example

Present-Tense Verb	Past-Tense Verb
Egyptians make the mummies.	Egyptians made the mummies.
The kings build pyramids.	The kings built pyramids.
The pyramids are made of stone.	The pyramids were made of stone.

► SUBJECT-VERB AGREEMENT

The **subject and verb** in a sentence must agree in number.

• A verb that agrees with a singular subject tells what one person, place, or thing is doing. It usually ends in *-s* or *-es*.
• A verb that agrees with a plural subject tells what more than one person, place, or thing is doing. It usually does not end in *-s* or *-es*.

Example

Singular Subject	Plural Subject
The marble rolls across the ground.	The marbles roll across the ground.
Lupe plays marbles.	We play marbles, too.

► USING SUBJECT AND OBJECT PRONOUNS

A **pronoun** is a word that takes the place of a noun in a sentence.

• Use a subject pronoun in the subject of a sentence.
• Use an object pronoun after a verb or after a word such as *for* or *to*.

Example

Subject Pronoun	Object Pronoun
I have a pet turtle.	My turtle likes me.
We got Myrtle at a pet adoption fair.	Myrtle crawled right up to us.
She eats lettuce for dinner.	Once, I gave a dead fly to her.

► USING ADJECTIVES THAT COMPARE

An **adjective** is a word that tells about or describes a noun. Adjectives can help compare two or more people or things.

- To use an adjective to compare two things, add -er to the adjective or use the word *more*.

- To use an adjective to compare three or more things, add -*est* to the adjectives or use the word *most*.

Example

Adjective Comparing Two Things	Adjective Comparing Three or More Things
Zac is stronger than his friend.	He is the strongest kid in his class.
Zac is more athletic than his friend.	He is the most athletic student in his class.

► USING ADVERBS

An **adjective** describes a person, place, or thing. An adverb describes a verb, an adjective, or another adverb. Many adverbs end in -*ly*.

- Use an adverb to make your writing more precise.

Example

Adjective	Adverb
Ruby went to a different school.	She was treated differently from whites.
There were unfair laws in many states.	Many people were treated unfairly.
Some brave people demanded justice.	They bravely stood up for their beliefs.

Usage and Mechanics

▶ USING END PUNCTUATION

Different kinds of sentences use different **end punctuation marks**.

- A **statement** always ends with a period.
- A **question** always ends with a question mark.

Example

Statement	Question
Firefighters have to be brave. A fire station is down the street.	Do you know a firefighter? Have you ever seen a fire?

▶ USING CAPITAL LETTERS

Some words begin with a **capital letter**.

- The first word in a sentence always begins with a capital letter.
- A proper noun always begins with a capital letter.

Example

Correct	Incorrect
The girls were all alone. The guard asked Virpal to stop.	the girls were all alone. The guard asked virpal to stop.

▶ USING CORRECT WORD ORDER

The **order of words** in a sentence must make sense.

- An adjective comes before the noun it describes.
- A helping verb comes just before the main verb in a statement.

Example

Correct	Incorrect
Bud liked what he was eating. Bud was a funny kid.	Bud liked what was he eating. Bud was a kid funny.

▶ USING COMMAS IN A SERIES

Items in a series are separated by **commas**.

• A series is a list of the same kinds of words.

• Commas follow every item in the series except the last one.

Example	
Correct	**Incorrect**
Kids, parents, and teachers all want bullying to end.	Kids parents and teachers all want bullying to end.

▶ USING COMMAS WITH INTRODUCTORY WORDS

A **comma** follows an opening word or phrase at the beginning of a sentence.

• *Yes, No, Next,* and *Later* are examples of opening words.

• *In addition* and *After a while* are examples of opening phrases.

Example	
Correct	**Incorrect**
Yes, King Tut was a pharaoh. After a while, they found the tomb.	Yes King Tut was a pharaoh. After a while they found the tomb.

▶ USING POSSESSIVE NOUNS

A **possessive noun** shows ownership.

• Add an apostrophe (') and an *-s* to a singular noun.

• Add an apostrophe to a plural noun that ends in *-s*.

Example	
Correct	**Incorrect**
Lupe's brother gave her advice. She looked at the marbles' colors.	Lupes brother gave her advice. She looked at the marbles colors.

► AVOIDING DOUBLE NEGATIVES

Negatives are words that express *no* or *not*.

- Use only one negative word to express a single negative idea.
- It is incorrect to use two negatives to express a negative idea.

Example

Correct	Incorrect
Tigers should never be pets. The alligator didn't eat anything.	Tigers shouldn't never be pets. The alligators didn't eat nothing.

► CORRECTING SENTENCE FRAGMENTS

Each sentence must state a complete idea.

- You can often add a subject or a verb to a sentence fragment to form a complete sentence.

Example

Correct	Incorrect
Zac changed his diet. He started walking more.	Changed his diet. [missing subject] He walking more. [missing verb]

► USING QUOTATION MARKS

Quotation marks show the exact words of a speaker.

- The first word of a quotation is capitalized.
- Punctuation usually goes inside the ending quotation mark.

Example

Correct	Incorrect
Annie asked, "Where is the milk?" "It's in the fridge," Yvonne said.	Annie asked, "where is the milk?" "It's in the fridge", Yvonne said.

How to Use the 21st Century Handbook

This handbook includes 21 skills that we all need for success in the 21st Century. These skills will help you in school, in your social life, and someday in your job or career.

Use this handbook to help you to complete the 21st Century Learning lessons and Wrap-Up Projects in the *rBook*. These skills will also be useful in other classes, such as science and social studies.

Table of Contents

 ## Make Decisions

How can you make the best choice? You can never be sure that any decision you make will be "right." But by following the right steps, you can make the best decision possible.

How do I decide?

► **Follow these steps:**

- **Clearly state the decision you need to make.** What are your options?
- **Gather information.** What do you need to know about the situation and each option? Whom can you ask?
- **Weigh pros and cons.** Which option has more positives? Which will have the best outcome?
- **Make your choice.** Try not to second-guess yourself.

Use IT!

At school: Some of your friends have joined the chess club. Should you?

At home: Should you go camping with a friend? You'll miss your dad's birthday.

Solve Problems

How do you face a problem? Ignore it? Sit down and put your head in your hands? There's no need to give up! With the right tools, you can solve almost any problem.

How can I solve this?

▶ **Follow these steps:**

- Collect information about the situation.
- State the problem clearly. Make sure you understand all parts of it.
- Brainstorm a few possible solutions. List the pros and cons of each.
- Choose a solution to try. Pick the one that seems most likely to work best.
- Try out your solution. If it doesn't work, figure out why and try something else.

Use IT!

At school: How can I go to the game *and* study for the test?

At home: Your parents can't drive you. How will you get to a friend's party?

Evaluate Risk

Taking risks is sometimes the only way to reach your goal. You might fail…but you might succeed. So take a risk, but ask yourself some questions before you take the first step.

Is it a good risk to take?

▶ **Ask yourself:**

- What are the possible rewards?
- What are the possible dangers?
- Is there a better way to reach my goal?
- What have other people done in similar situations? How has it worked out?
- Can I protect myself if I take this risk? How?

Use IT!

At school: Should I try out for school patrol officer?

At home: Do I need to wear a bike helmet? Why or why not?

Set Criteria

How can you decide what passes the test? If you want to decide which book to read or what to have for lunch to stay healthy, be sure you set your standards, or criteria.

What standards should I use?

▶ **Use these tips:**

- Make sure you are comparing similar items.
- Decide what qualities are most important to you.
- Make a scale, from 1 to 5, for each quality you want to compare.
- Be honest and fair when you use your criteria to make a judgment.

> **Use IT!** **At school:** Set criteria for working together as a group.
>
> **At home:** Set criteria for staying healthy and being helpful to others.

Justify a Point of View

Everyone has an opinion. But not everyone knows how to convince others to listen. If you want your opinion to be heard, state your case with power.

How can I support my opinion?

▶ **Use these tips:**

- **Reasons.** Make your point by explaining clearly why you believe as you do.
- **Facts and numbers.** Facts and numbers are more convincing than words alone. Do your research, and share what you learn. The results will be worth it.
- **Examples.** Persuade others with examples that support your opinion.
- **Expert backup.** Is there an expert who believes what you do? Use that person's opinion to support your own.

> **Use IT!** **At school:** Did you love or hate the book you read? Explain why.
>
> **At home:** Do you deserve more computer time? Convince your family.

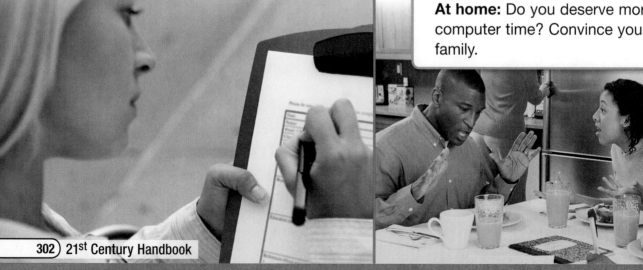

⊗ Understand Different Points of View

There's more than one side to every story. To settle a situation where everyone disagrees, try to understand each point of view.

Can we understand each other better?

▶ **Follow these steps:**

- **Figure out what each side believes.** Restate each person's side of the story in your own words.
- **Consider why he or she feels that way.** What information is each person using? How is his or her attitude related to life experiences and personal beliefs?
- **Evaluate what you've heard.** Which opinions and reasons do you think are easiest to believe?
- **Decide which viewpoint you agree with, and why.** Even if you disagree with someone, at least you'll understand the person better.

Use IT! **At school:** Understand school rules from more than one side.

At home: See an argument through a family member's eyes.

❓ Ask Questions

How do we get the answers we need? We ask questions! You can use different types of questions to get the information you need, when you need it.

What do I ask?

▶ **Ask yourself:**

- **Recall and understand:** What do I need to know? What have I learned?
- **Apply:** How can I use this information?
- **Analyze:** What are the parts or steps? Why does it occur?
- **Synthesize:** How can I combine what I've learned into a new idea?
- **Evaluate:** How good is it? What evidence supports it?

Use IT! **At school:** Can I restate what the teacher is talking about?

At home: Is that new cell phone worth the money?

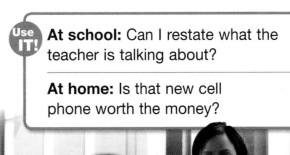

✺ Resolve Conflicts

Conflict is a part of life. At some point, we all disagree with someone. Here's how to find a solution that feels fair to everyone involved.

How can we work this out?

▶ **Follow these steps:**

- Restate the conflict in your own words.
- Allow each individual or group to tell their version of the story or situation.
- Brainstorm solutions.
- Decide on a solution or course of action that everyone can agree on.
- Follow up. Make sure the solution is put into action and that everyone does what he or she should.

Use IT! **At school:** Offer a solution during an argument between two students.

At home: Work to get family members to agree on an issue.

🔲 Present Effectively

You *will* be speaking in front of a group. Whether it's an oral report in class or an update you'll give at work someday, make it a presentation they'll remember.

What's the secret of a good presentation?

▶ **Use these tips:**

- Do you need to inform, entertain, or persuade? Your purpose will affect what you present, and how you present it.
- Know what you're talking about. Do the research. Get solid information.
- Use visuals. Photographs, slide shows, maps, and graphs can add interest.
- Use your eyes and voice. Look at listeners often. Speak loudly and clearly.

Use IT! **At school:** Deliver your presentation so everyone will listen.

At home: Entertain others with a slide show about a recent event.

Build a Team

People need to work together. But not every team can get the job done. You need a team that can work together to accomplish goals.

How can we build a good team?

▶ **Follow these steps:**

- Clarify your goals. Brainstorm a list of tasks.
- Discuss who would be the best person for each job.
- Follow up on the work. Is everyone doing what he or she should?
- Work through problems as a team.

> **Use IT!** **At school:** Do a group science experiment.
>
> **At home:** Hold a group tag sale.

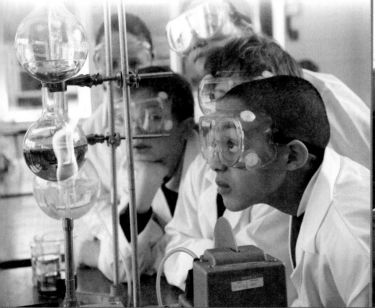

Brainstorming

Think "outside the box." When you let your mind explore many possibilities, you can solve problems, gather cool and useful facts, and end up with a bunch of great ideas.

What are the possibilities?

▶ **Use these tips:**

- **Let it flow.** The purpose of brainstorming is to gather many ideas quickly. Let your mind go in many directions, and jot down ideas as they come to you.
- **Use 5 Ws and an H.** Get your mind going by asking questions that begin with *who, what, when, where, why,* and *how.*
- **Write now, judge later!** Write quickly to keep the ideas flowing. You can go back later to choose your best idea, or to polish what you have written.

> **Use IT!** **At school:** Come up with an idea for a group project.
>
> **At home:** Figure out a perfect system for organizing your stuff.

Think Creatively

> **Writing stories is one way to be creative. Painting and playing music are other ways.** Learn how you can be more inventive.

How can I use my creativity?

▶ **Use these tips:**

- **Identify your goal.** Are you writing a play? Working on a social studies project? What do you want to achieve?

- **Think outside the box.** Use your brainstorming skills. Be open to new ideas. Ask yourself, "What's the opposite of that idea?"

- **Put your ideas to work.** Try out an idea. If it doesn't work, decide what part to change. Change it, then try again.

 At school: Use your imagination to write a story.

At home: Design a new game.

 Find a Mentor

> **Everyone has special talents and experiences.** A mentor can provide advice to help you reach your goals. Find a mentor who is right for you.

Who can help me get to where I want to be?

▶ **Follow these steps:**

- **Identify a need.** What do you want a mentor to help you achieve?

- **Search for mentors.** See if your school has a mentoring program. Outside of school, ask an adult to help you find a pro who works in a field that interests you.

- **Contact possible mentors.** Be clear about what you're looking for. Ask questions.

- **Create a plan.** With your new mentor, set goals. Then make a plan to reach them.

- **Be polite.** Always thank your mentor for his or her time.

At school: Learn about the jobs of people who work in your school.

At home: Find a family member who can tell you about his or her career.

 Set Goals

We all have dreams and goals. But sometimes they never become real. Here's how you can turn goals into something real.

How can I achieve my goals?

▶ **Follow these steps:**

- Set a goal that is specific and doable.
- List tasks that will get you to your goal.
- Research each task. Try to talk to someone who has met the same goal.
- Set a deadline for reaching your goal and tasks along the way.
- Give yourself a pat on the back for completing each step toward your goal.

> **Use IT!** **At school:** I want to get all A's next grading period.
>
> **At home:** I want to have more chores and a bigger allowance.

Gather Information

We live in the Information Age. Technology tools bring a lot of information to our fingertips. Here's how to find the knowledge you need.

How do I get information I need?

▶ **Use these tips:**

- **Know what you need.** Get focused by framing your question or goal clearly.
- **Use a search engine.** Try different search terms to find sources online.
- **Be imaginative.** Some sources that are available are charts, tables, schedules, reviews, images, and lists. Look for these and evaluate them.
- **Use multiple methods.** Branch out from the Web. How? Use library books, conduct a survey, or interview an expert.

> **Use IT!** **At school:** Where can I find ideas for an unusual project?
>
> **At home:** Has a student my age begun a successful business?

Take Notes

How will you remember important information? Take notes. Learn how to take and organize notes for easy access to the information you need.

How can I take good notes?

▶ **Take these steps:**

- **Figure out what you need to know.** Do you need to remember dates in history? Steps in a process? Do you need to learn about an author?
- **Get the information you need.** Explore many sources: books, websites, videos, local experts, and more.
- **Write it down.** Write down the main points. Circle or underline what you most need to remember.
- **Organize.** While the information is still fresh, make sure you understand what you wrote or typed. Put your notes in an order you can use later.

 At school: Write a paper filled with interesting facts and ideas.

At home: Save important details about events that matter to you.

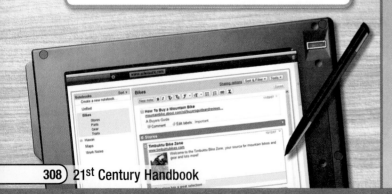

Analyze Media

You see thousands of media messages every day. Ads, newspapers, books, movies, websites—what are they telling you? Figure out the message behind the media.

What are they trying to tell me?

▶ **Ask yourself:**

- Who created the message and why?
- What images and words do they use?
- What information and ideas are included in this message? What is left out?
- Is the message reliable? Why or why not?

Use IT! **At school:** Gather reliable sources for a speech.

At home: Figure out whether an ad is too good to be true.

Analyze Information

 # Evaluate Sources

Information is all around us. To use all that incoming information, we need to determine what we can learn from as we read or listen. Learn to analyze patterns of information.

You can't believe everything you read. When it comes to both print and online sources, separate the useful from the useless.

What can I learn from this source?

Can I trust this information?

▶ **Ask yourself:**

- What is the topic of this information?
- What is the main idea about the topic?
- How is this information organized? By cause and effect? By problem and solution? By time order?
- How new to me is this information? Is it similar to other things I've read or heard about this topic?

▶ **Ask yourself:**

- Is the source current? If it's a website, was it recently updated?
- Is the author or publisher an expert on the topic?
- Is the source unbiased?
- Does the content seem well written, well researched, and logical?

 Use IT!

At school: Understand science articles. Use a diagram, table, or chart.

At home: Read maps, recipes, instructions, and schedules.

 Use IT!

At school: Find reliable info sources.

At home: Find a dependable review of that new video game.

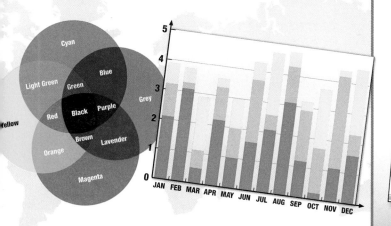

🌐 Use the Internet

We practically live online. In fact, people spend hours every day visiting websites. Learn how to create a web page that people want to visit.

What makes people want to visit and read a web page?

▶ **Use these tips:**

- Decide on your purpose, and make it clear to those who visit your web page.
- Find a free template online. Search for "web page templates."
- Create a banner that will identify your page and create interest.
- Organize your page with clear headings and bulleted lists.
- Choose colors and fonts that go well with your content.

> **Use IT!** **At school:** Create a home page for your club or team.
>
> **At home:** Create your own blog.

⭐ Use Technology for Communication

Technology keeps changing the way people communicate. We need to make sure we choose the technology tool that will give the best results.

How can I share my ideas?

▶ **Use these tips:**

- There are many ways to tell someone about a good idea or give someone information.
- A text message or cell phone call can alert your parents about what time to pick you up after school.
- Email messages are a good way to give someone a suggestion.
- To share information and ideas with groups of people, start a blog, create a web page, or present a slide show.

> **Use IT!** **At school:** Hold a video conference with students at another school.
>
> **At home:** Start an e-club for a hobby that interests you.

rBook Workshop Log

▶ Fill in the dates that you start and complete each Workshop. Rate your effort on the Workshop using the Rating Scale. Record the date and your score for the rSkills Test. Then write a final statement about the Workshop.

Rating Guide			
needs improvement	average	good	excellent
①	②	③	④

WORKSHOP 1 — Fires Out of Control

Date Started	Date Completed

Self-Assessment
Rate your effort during this Workshop.
① ② ③ ④

What would you do if a fire was headed toward your neighborhood?

_____

_____

_____

rSkills Test   Date: _____   Score: _____

WORKSHOP 2 — Coming to America

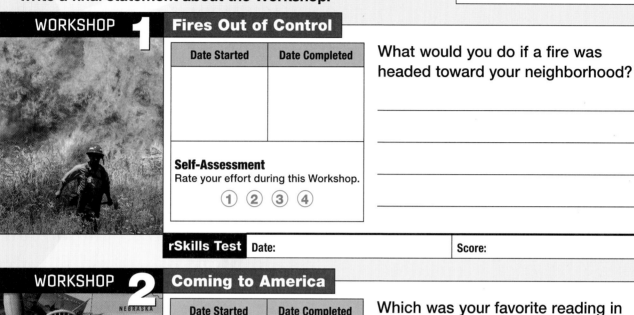

Date Started	Date Completed

Self-Assessment
Rate your effort during this Workshop.
① ② ③ ④

Which was your favorite reading in this Workshop?
☐ "New to the U.S."
☐ "My Journey to America"
☐ "A Nation of Immigrants"

Why? _____

_____

rSkills Test   Date: _____   Score: _____

WORKSHOP 3 — Bud, Not Buddy

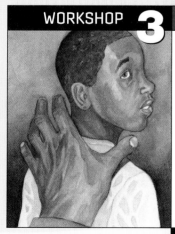

Date Started	Date Completed

Self-Assessment
Rate your effort during this Workshop.
① ② ③ ④

Do you think it was fair for the "pretend family" to help Bud? Why or why not?

_____

_____

_____

rSkills Test   Date: _____   Score: _____

WORKSHOP 4 — Bullies Beware

Date Started	Date Completed

Self-Assessment
Rate your effort during this Workshop.
① ② ③ ④

What do you think is a good way to stop a bully?

_____

_____

_____

_____

_____

rSkills Test Date: _____ Score: _____

WORKSHOP 5 — Secrets of the Mummy's Tomb

Date Started	Date Completed

Self-Assessment
Rate your effort during this Workshop.
① ② ③ ④

Which of the following things would you most like to see in person?

❑ a mummy
❑ a pyramid
❑ a sealed door inside a tomb

Why? _____

_____

_____

rSkills Test Date: _____ Score: _____

WORKSHOP 6 — Good Sports

Date Started	Date Completed

Self-Assessment
Rate your effort during this Workshop.
① ② ③ ④

Would you want to be friends with Lupe? Why or why not? Explain.

_____

_____

_____

_____

rSkills Test Date: _____ Score: _____

WORKSHOP 7 — Taming Wild Beasts

Date Started	Date Completed

Self-Assessment
Rate your effort during this Workshop.
① ② ③ ④

Which animal would you *least* want to have as a pet?

❑ a gorilla ❑ an alligator
❑ a tiger ❑ a polar bear

Why? _____
_____
_____
_____

rSkills Test Date: _____ Score: _____

WORKSHOP 8 — Food: The Good, the Bad, and the Gross

Date Started	Date Completed

Self-Assessment
Rate your effort during this Workshop.
① ② ③ ④

You know that bugs can be healthy food . . . but would you ever eat one? Why or why not?

_____
_____
_____
_____
_____

rSkills Test Date: _____ Score: _____

WORKSHOP 9 — No Small Hero

Date Started	Date Completed

Self-Assessment
Rate your effort during this Workshop.
① ② ③ ④

If you could ask Ruby Bridges one question, what would you ask?

_____
_____
_____
_____
_____

rSkills Test Date: _____ Score: _____

Topic Software Log

▶ Use these pages to keep track of the Topics you have completed. Check off each segment you finish. Then write a final statement about each Topic.

Topic 1 Can You Believe It?

- ☐ 1.1 *Crazy Horse*
- ☐ 1.2 *Polar Bears*
- ☐ 1.3 *Art Cars*
- ☐ 1.4 *I'm No Clown*

The artist or work of art I'd really like to see in person is _____
_____

Topic 2 Predators

- ☐ 2.1 *Built to Kill!*
- ☐ 2.2 *Super Senses*
- ☐ 2.3 *Deadly Droolers*
- ☐ 2.4 *Dinnertime!*

The grossest thing I saw in these videos was _____
_____

Topic 3 Mummies, Bones, and Garbage

- ☐ 3.1 *The Great Dino Debate*
- ☐ 3.2 *Mysteries of the Mummy*
- ☐ 3.3 *Ancient Guards*
- ☐ 3.4 *Tracing Trash*

The most interesting thing I saw in this Topic was _____
_____

Topic 4 It's How You Play the Game

- ☐ 4.1 *No Snow? No Problem!*
- ☐ 4.2 *On Your Mark*
- ☐ 4.3 *Let the Games Begin*
- ☐ 4.4 *Coop Can Shoot*

One new thing I learned was _____
_____

Topic 5 Thrills and Chills

- ☐ 5.1 *Movie Magic*
- ☐ 5.2 *Do the Math*
- ☐ 5.3 *Big Spending*
- ☐ 5.4 *Wild Ride*

My favorite segment was _____
_____

Topic 6 *One Man's March: Martin Luther King Jr.*

- ☐ 6.1 *A Young Man With a Dream*
- ☐ 6.2 *The Montgomery Bus Boycott*
- ☐ 6.3 *The March on Washington*
- ☐ 6.4 *I Have a Dream*

The thing I admire most about Martin Luther King Jr. is _____

_____

_____

Topic 7 *Forgotten Heroes*

- ☐ 7.1 *Los Mineros*
- ☐ 7.2 *Playing Hardball*
- ☐ 7.3 *The Men of the 54th*
- ☐ 7.4 *Uniting the States*

The most heroic group of people in this Topic is _____

_____

_____

Topic 8 *Weird Science*

- ☐ 8.1 *Shocking!*
- ☐ 8.2 *Killer Plants*
- ☐ 8.3 *Bat Attack*
- ☐ 8.4 *Winged Wonders*

The coolest thing I saw was _____

_____

_____

Topic 9 *History Mysteries*

- ☐ 9.1 *Secrets of Stonehenge*
- ☐ 9.2 *Mayan Mystery*
- ☐ 9.3 *Lost in Flight*
- ☐ 9.4 *Titanic's Forgotten Sister*

The most mysterious story was _____

_____

_____

Topic 10 *Myths and Monsters*

- ☐ 10.1 *Phaeton's Wild Ride*
- ☐ 10.2 *Dragon Tales*
- ☐ 10.3 *The Legend of Lucia*
- ☐ 10.4 *Frankenstein Lives!*

I think a good movie could be made about _____

_____

_____

Topic 11 It's the Write Job

- ☐ 11.1 **Sports Report**
- ☐ 11.2 **Wizard of Words**
- ☐ 11.3 **Toy Story**
- ☐ 11.4 **On the Beat**

The job I'm most interested in for myself is _____

_____

_____

Topic 12 Beyond Words!

- ☐ 12.1 **"The Greatest"**
- ☐ 12.2 **Under a Spell**
- ☐ 12.3 **It's a Good Sign**
- ☐ 12.4 **War of Words**

I would recommend this Topic to _____

_____

_____

Topic 13 Now You See It...

- ☐ 13.1 **Elephants Never Forget**
- ☐ 13.2 **On Thin Ice**
- ☐ 13.3 **Gulf Bird Watch**
- ☐ 13.4 **Flight of the Monarch**

The most amazing thing I saw was _____

_____

_____

Topic 14 The Wow Factor

- ☐ 14.1 **Star Power**
- ☐ 14.2 **Escape Artist**
- ☐ 14.3 **Top Dog**
- ☐ 14.4 **A Force of Nature**

The story that I keep thinking about the most is _____

_____

_____

Topic 15 Tech Time

- ☐ 15.1 **Robot Nation**
- ☐ 15.2 **In the Deep**
- ☐ 15.3 **Trapped!**
- ☐ 15.4 **Spare Parts**

One new thing I learned about technology was _____

_____

_____

Independent Reading Log

▶ **Use these pages to keep track of the texts you read.**

- Write the title in the blank box. Add a design if you like.
- Fill in the dates that you started and completed each text.
- Mark what kind of text it is.
- Rate the text using the rating scale at right. Then write a statement about it.

Rating Scale

★★★★ = It was excellent!
★★★☆ = It was good.
★★☆☆ = It was okay.
★☆☆☆ = I didn't like it.

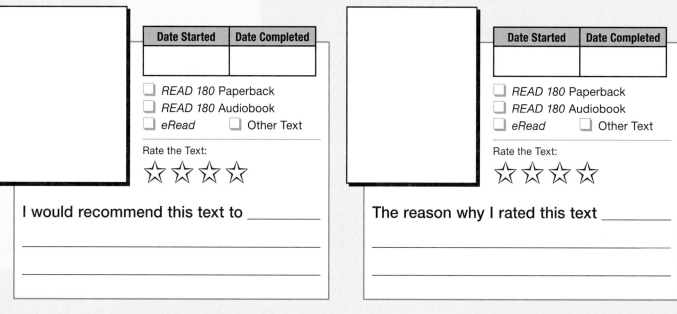

Date Started	Date Completed

☐ *READ 180* Paperback
☐ *READ 180* Audiobook
☐ *eRead*   ☐ Other Text

Rate the Text:
☆ ☆ ☆ ☆

I would recommend this text to _____
_____
_____

Date Started	Date Completed

☐ *READ 180* Paperback
☐ *READ 180* Audiobook
☐ *eRead*   ☐ Other Text

Rate the Text:
☆ ☆ ☆ ☆

The reason why I rated this text _____
_____
_____

Date Started	Date Completed

☐ *READ 180* Paperback
☐ *READ 180* Audiobook
☐ *eRead*   ☐ Other Text

Rate the Text:
☆ ☆ ☆ ☆

This text reminded me of _____
_____
_____

Date Started	Date Completed

☐ *READ 180* Paperback
☐ *READ 180* Audiobook
☐ *eRead*   ☐ Other Text

Rate the Text:
☆ ☆ ☆ ☆

I chose to read this text because _____
_____
_____

Date Started	Date Completed

☐ *READ 180* Paperback
☐ *READ 180* Audiobook
☐ *eRead*　　☐ Other Text

Rate the Text:
⭐⭐⭐☆

One question I have for the author is _____

_____

_____

Date Started	Date Completed

☐ *READ 180* Paperback
☐ *READ 180* Audiobook
☐ *eRead*　　☐ Other Text

Rate the Text:
⭐⭐⭐☆

I think I will/will not remember this text

because _____

_____

Date Started	Date Completed

☐ *READ 180* Paperback
☐ *READ 180* Audiobook
☐ *eRead*　　☐ Other Text

Rate the Text:
☆☆☆☆

The best part of this text was _____

_____

_____

Date Started	Date Completed

☐ *READ 180* Paperback
☐ *READ 180* Audiobook
☐ *eRead*　　☐ Other Text

Rate the Text:
☆☆☆☆

One new thing I learned in this text was _____

_____

_____

Date Started	Date Completed

☐ *READ 180* Paperback
☐ *READ 180* Audiobook
☐ *eRead*　　☐ Other Text

Rate the Text:
☆☆☆☆

If I were making this text into a movie, it

would star _____

_____

Date Started	Date Completed

☐ *READ 180* Paperback
☐ *READ 180* Audiobook
☐ *eRead*　　☐ Other Text

Rate the Text:
☆☆☆☆

This text was easy/hard to finish because

_____

_____

Date Started	Date Completed

- [ ] *READ 180* Paperback
- [ ] *READ 180* Audiobook
- [ ] *eRead*   [ ] Other Text

Rate the Text:
☆ ☆ ☆ ☆

If I were making this text into a movie, it would star _____

_____

Date Started	Date Completed

- [ ] *READ 180* Paperback
- [ ] *READ 180* Audiobook
- [ ] *eRead*   [ ] Other Text

Rate the Text:
☆ ☆ ☆ ☆

When I first saw this text, I thought it would be _____

_____

Date Started	Date Completed

- [ ] *READ 180* Paperback
- [ ] *READ 180* Audiobook
- [ ] *eRead*   [ ] Other Text

Rate the Text:
☆ ☆ ☆ ☆

I'd recommend this text to _____

_____

Date Started	Date Completed

- [ ] *READ 180* Paperback
- [ ] *READ 180* Audiobook
- [ ] *eRead*   [ ] Other Text

Rate the Text:
☆ ☆ ☆ ☆

Reading this text made me feel _____

_____

Date Started	Date Completed

- [ ] *READ 180* Paperback
- [ ] *READ 180* Audiobook
- [ ] *eRead*   [ ] Other Text

Rate the Text:
☆ ☆ ☆ ☆

The most interesting thing about this text was _____

_____

Date Started	Date Completed

- [ ] *READ 180* Paperback
- [ ] *READ 180* Audiobook
- [ ] *eRead*   [ ] Other Text

Rate the Text:
☆ ☆ ☆ ☆

One fact I learned in this text is _____

_____

Date Started	Date Completed

- ☐ *READ 180* Paperback
- ☐ *READ 180* Audiobook
- ☐ eRead   ☐ Other Text

Rate the Text:
★ ★ ★ ☆

The best thing about this text is _____

_____

_____

Date Started	Date Completed

- ☐ *READ 180* Paperback
- ☐ *READ 180* Audiobook
- ☐ eRead   ☐ Other Text

Rate the Text:
★ ★ ★ ☆

Three words that describe this text are _____

_____

_____

Date Started	Date Completed

- ☐ *READ 180* Paperback
- ☐ *READ 180* Audiobook
- ☐ eRead   ☐ Other Text

Rate the Text:
☆ ☆ ☆ ☆

I would recommend this text to _____

_____

_____

Date Started	Date Completed

- ☐ *READ 180* Paperback
- ☐ *READ 180* Audiobook
- ☐ eRead   ☐ Other Text

Rate the Text:
☆ ☆ ☆ ☆

This text should/should not have a sequel because _____

_____

Date Started	Date Completed

- ☐ *READ 180* Paperback
- ☐ *READ 180* Audiobook
- ☐ eRead   ☐ Other Text

Rate the Text:
☆ ☆ ☆ ☆

If I were making this text into a movie, it would star _____

_____

Date Started	Date Completed

- ☐ *READ 180* Paperback
- ☐ *READ 180* Audiobook
- ☐ eRead   ☐ Other Text

Rate the Text:
☆ ☆ ☆ ☆

One new thing I learned in this text is _____

_____

_____

Date Started	Date Completed

☐ *READ 180* Paperback
☐ *READ 180* Audiobook
☐ *eRead*   ☐ Other Text

Rate the Text:
☆ ☆ ☆ ☆

If I were making this text into a movie, it would star _____

_____

Date Started	Date Completed

☐ *READ 180* Paperback
☐ *READ 180* Audiobook
☐ *eRead*   ☐ Other Text

Rate the Text:
☆ ☆ ☆ ☆

When I first saw this text, I thought it would be _____

_____

Date Started	Date Completed

☐ *READ 180* Paperback
☐ *READ 180* Audiobook
☐ *eRead*   ☐ Other Text

Rate the Text:
☆ ☆ ☆ ☆

I would recommend this text to _____

_____

_____

Date Started	Date Completed

☐ *READ 180* Paperback
☐ *READ 180* Audiobook
☐ *eRead*   ☐ Other Text

Rate the Text:
☆ ☆ ☆ ☆

The reason why I rated this text _____

_____

_____

Date Started	Date Completed

☐ *READ 180* Paperback
☐ *READ 180* Audiobook
☐ *eRead*   ☐ Other Text

Rate the Text:
☆ ☆ ☆ ☆

This text reminds me of _____

_____

_____

Date Started	Date Completed

☐ *READ 180* Paperback
☐ *READ 180* Audiobook
☐ *eRead*   ☐ Other Text

Rate the Text:
☆ ☆ ☆ ☆

I chose to read this text because _____

_____

_____

Date Started	Date Completed

☐ *READ 180* Paperback
☐ *READ 180* Audiobook
☐ *eRead*   ☐ Other Text

Rate the Text:
☆☆☆☆

One question I have for the author is _____
_____
_____

Date Started	Date Completed

☐ *READ 180* Paperback
☐ *READ 180* Audiobook
☐ *eRead*   ☐ Other Text

Rate the Text:
☆☆☆☆

I think I will/will not remember this text because _____
_____

Date Started	Date Completed

☐ *READ 180* Paperback
☐ *READ 180* Audiobook
☐ *eRead*   ☐ Other Text

Rate the Text:
☆☆☆☆

The best part of this text is _____
_____
_____

Date Started	Date Completed

☐ *READ 180* Paperback
☐ *READ 180* Audiobook
☐ *eRead*   ☐ Other Text

Rate the Text:
☆☆☆☆

One new thing I learned in this text is _____
_____
_____

Date Started	Date Completed

☐ *READ 180* Paperback
☐ *READ 180* Audiobook
☐ *eRead*   ☐ Other Text

Rate the Text:
☆☆☆☆

If I were making this text into a movie, it would star _____
_____

Date Started	Date Completed

☐ *READ 180* Paperback
☐ *READ 180* Audiobook
☐ *eRead*   ☐ Other Text

Rate the Text:
☆☆☆☆

This text was easy/hard to finish because
_____
_____

Date Started	Date Completed

❑ *READ 180* Paperback
❑ *READ 180* Audiobook
❑ *eRead*   ❑ Other Text

Rate the Text:
☆ ☆ ☆ ☆

I will/will not read more texts like this one
because _____
_____

Date Started	Date Completed

❑ *READ 180* Paperback
❑ *READ 180* Audiobook
❑ *eRead*   ❑ Other Text

Rate the Text:
☆ ☆ ☆ ☆

When I first saw this text, I thought it
would be _____
_____

Date Started	Date Completed

❑ *READ 180* Paperback
❑ *READ 180* Audiobook
❑ *eRead*   ❑ Other Text

Rate the Text:
☆ ☆ ☆ ☆

I'd recommend this text to _____
_____
_____

Date Started	Date Completed

❑ *READ 180* Paperback
❑ *READ 180* Audiobook
❑ *eRead*   ❑ Other Text

Rate the Text:
☆ ☆ ☆ ☆

Reading this text made me feel _____
_____
_____

Date Started	Date Completed

❑ *READ 180* Paperback
❑ *READ 180* Audiobook
❑ *eRead*   ❑ Other Text

Rate the Text:
☆ ☆ ☆ ☆

The most interesting thing about this text
is _____
_____

Date Started	Date Completed

❑ *READ 180* Paperback
❑ *READ 180* Audiobook
❑ *eRead*   ❑ Other Text

Rate the Text:
☆ ☆ ☆ ☆

One fact I learned from this text is _____
_____
_____

Date Started	Date Completed

☐ *READ 180* Paperback
☐ *READ 180* Audiobook
☐ *eRead*   ☐ Other Text

Rate the Text:
☆ ☆ ☆ ☆

The best thing about this text is _____

_____

_____

Date Started	Date Completed

☐ *READ 180* Paperback
☐ *READ 180* Audiobook
☐ *eRead*   ☐ Other Text

Rate the Text:
☆ ☆ ☆ ☆

Three words that describe this text are _____

_____

_____

Date Started	Date Completed

☐ *READ 180* Paperback
☐ *READ 180* Audiobook
☐ *eRead*   ☐ Other Text

Rate the Text:
☆ ☆ ☆ ☆

I would recommend this text to _____

_____

_____

Date Started	Date Completed

☐ *READ 180* Paperback
☐ *READ 180* Audiobook
☐ *eRead*   ☐ Other Text

Rate the Text:
☆ ☆ ☆ ☆

This text should/should not have a sequel

because _____

_____

Date Started	Date Completed

☐ *READ 180* Paperback
☐ *READ 180* Audiobook
☐ *eRead*   ☐ Other Text

Rate the Text:
☆ ☆ ☆ ☆

I could/could not put this text down

because _____

_____

Date Started	Date Completed

☐ *READ 180* Paperback
☐ *READ 180* Audiobook
☐ *eRead*   ☐ Other Text

Rate the Text:
☆ ☆ ☆ ☆

One new thing I learned from this text is ___

_____

_____

Keep Track of Your Success!

▶ Create a bar graph showing your SRI Lexile scores over the year.

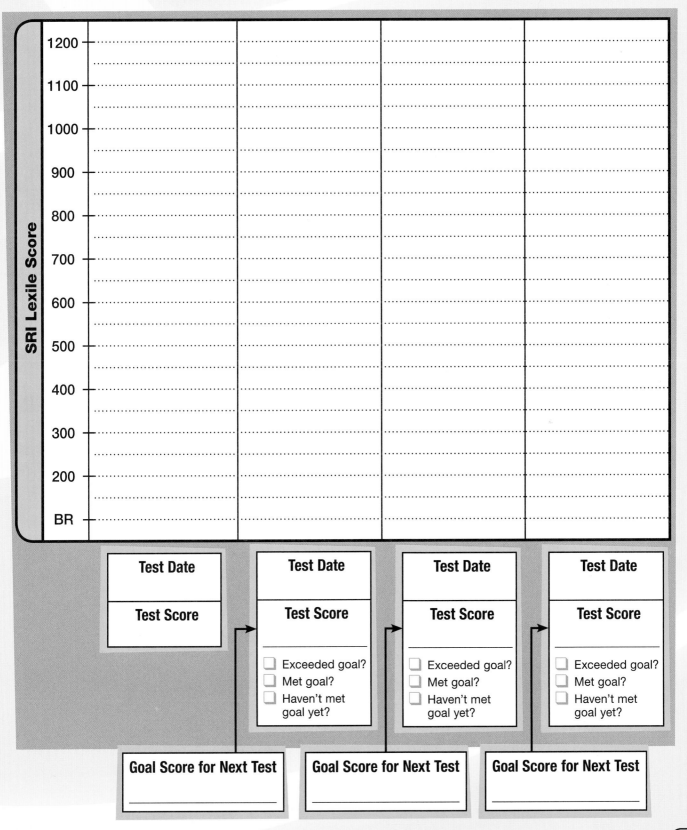

SRI Lexile Score

1200
1100
1000
900
800
700
600
500
400
300
200
BR

Test Date	Test Date	Test Date	Test Date
Test Score	**Test Score**	**Test Score**	**Test Score**
	☐ Exceeded goal? ☐ Met goal? ☐ Haven't met goal yet?	☐ Exceeded goal? ☐ Met goal? ☐ Haven't met goal yet?	☐ Exceeded goal? ☐ Met goal? ☐ Haven't met goal yet?

Goal Score for Next Test

Goal Score for Next Test

Goal Score for Next Test

ACKNOWLEDGMENTS

Grateful acknowledgment is made to the following sources for permission to reprint from previously published material. The publisher has made diligent efforts to trace the ownership of all copyrighted material in this volume and believes that all necessary permissions have been secured. If any errors or omissions have inadvertently been made, proper corrections will gladly be made in future editions.

Workshop 2
Coming to America

"New to the U.S." adapted from "A New World" by Rebecca Thatcher Murcia from *Scholastic News Senior Edition* magazine, September 29, 2003. Copyright © 2003 by Scholastic Inc. All rights reserved.

"My Journey to America" adapted from "Virpal" from Scholastic News Online. Copyright © 2004 by Scholastic Inc. All rights reserved.

Workshop 3
Bud, Not Buddy

"Bud's Breakfast" adapted from *Bud, Not Buddy* by Christopher Paul Curtis. Copyright © 1999 by Christopher Paul Curtis. Reprinted by permission of Random House Children's Books, a division of Random House, Inc.

Cover from *The Watsons Go to Birmingham—1963* by Christopher Paul Curtis. Copyright © 1995 by Christopher Paul Curtis. Used by permission of Random House Children's Books, a division of Random House, Inc.

Workshop 4
Bullies Beware

Adapted from "Girl Fight" by Karen Fanning from *Scholastic Choices* magazine, October 2002. Copyright © 2002 by Scholastic Inc. All rights reserved.

Workshop 6
Good Sports

"The Marble Champ" from *Baseball in April and Other Stories* by Gary Soto. Copyright © 1990 by Gary Soto. Reprinted by permission of Harcourt, Inc.

"Biography of Gary Soto" and author photo from The Official Gary Soto Web Site (http://www.garysoto.com). Reprinted by permission of Gary Soto.

"S-T-R-E-T-C-H" from *The Last-Place Sports Poems of Jeremy Bloom* by Gordon Korman and Bernice Korman. Copyright © 1996 by Gordon Korman and Bernice Korman. Reprinted by permission of Scholastic Inc. All rights reserved.

Workshop 9
No Small Hero

Text and cover from *Through My Eyes* by Ruby Bridges. Copyright © 1999 by Ruby Bridges. Reprinted by permission of Scholastic Press, a division of Scholastic Inc. Cover: AP/Wide World.

"Life Doesn't Frighten Me" from *And Still I Rise* by Maya Angelou. Copyright © 1978 by Maya Angelou. Reprinted by permission of Random House, Inc.